STUDENT LECTURE NOTEBOOK

ESSENTIALS OF OCEANOGRAPHY

EIGHTH EDITION

Alan P. Trujillo • *Harold V. Thurman*

PEARSON

Prentice
Hall

Upper Saddle River, NJ 07458

Assistant Editor: Melanie Cutler
Executive Editor: Patrick Lynch
Editor-in-Chief, Science: John Challice
Vice President of Production & Manufacturing: David W. Riccardi
Executive Managing Editor: Kathleen Schiaparelli
Assistant Managing Editor: Becca Richter
Production Editor: Dana Dunn
Supplement Cover Management/Design: Paul Gourhan
Supplement Cover Designer: Christopher Kossa
Manufacturing Buyer: Michael Bell
Cover Photo Credit: Norbert Wu / Minden Pictures

© 2005 Pearson Education, Inc.
Pearson Prentice Hall
Pearson Education, Inc.
Upper Saddle River, NJ 07458

Printed in the United States of America

10 9 8 7 6 5 4 3 2 1

ISBN 0-13-144780-7

Pearson Education Ltd., *London*
Pearson Education Australia Pty. Ltd., *Sydney*
Pearson Education Singapore, Pte. Ltd.
Pearson Education North Asia Ltd., *Hong Kong*
Pearson Education Canada, Inc., *Toronto*
Pearson Educación de Mexico, S.A. de C.V.
Pearson Education—Japan, *Tokyo*
Pearson Education Malaysia, Pte. Ltd.

CONTENTS

This *Student Lecture Notebook* is designed to help you do your best in this oceanography course.

Key images from the textbook and every illustration from the Instructor's Transparency Set are reproduced in this notebook. Because you won't have to redraw the art in class, you can focus your attention on the lecture, annotate the art, and take your notes in this book.

Leave all your notes together or remove them for integration into a binder with other course materials.

NOTES:

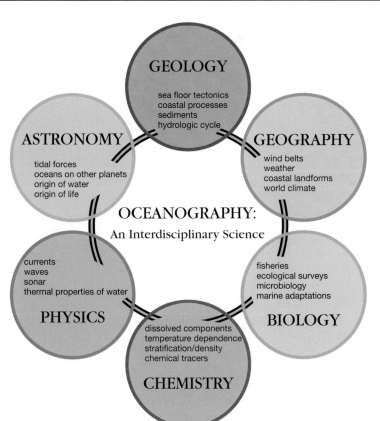

Figure I.2   Venn diagram showing the interdisciplinary nature of oceanography

NOTES:

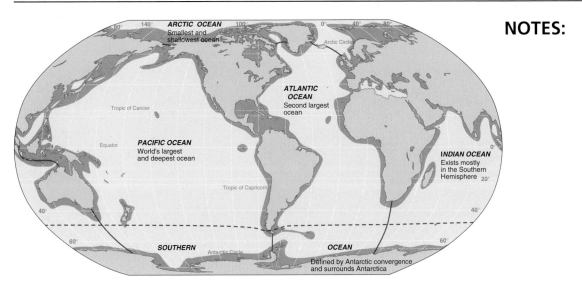

Figure 1.2   Earth's oceans

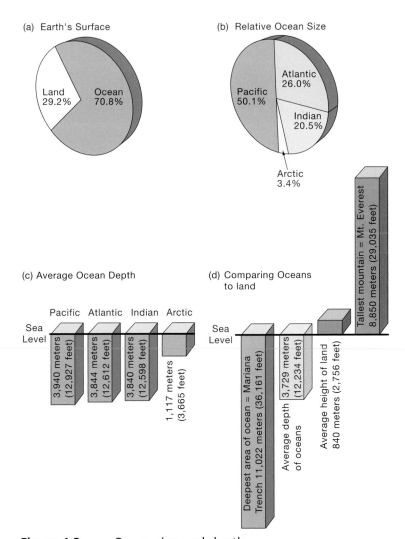

Figure 1.3   Ocean size and depth

NOTES:

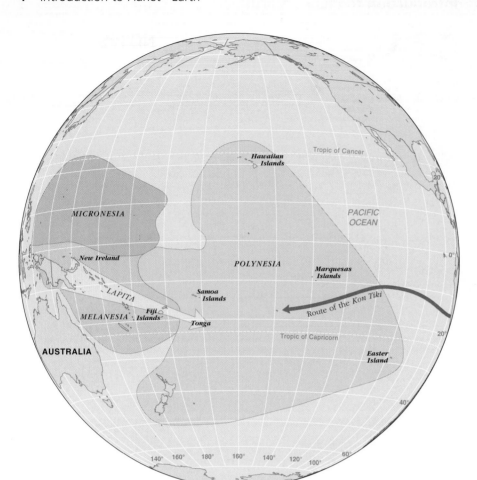

Figure 1.5   The peopling of the Pacific islands

Figure 1.6   Viking colonies in the North Atlantic

NOTES:

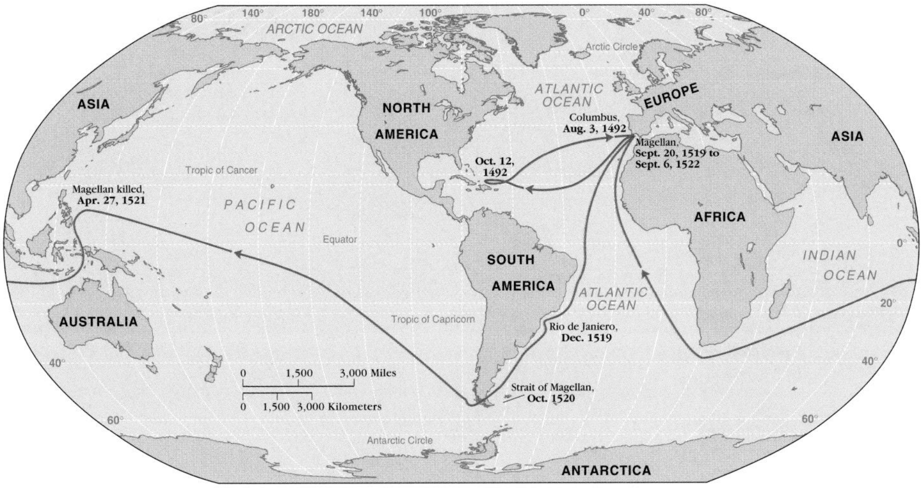

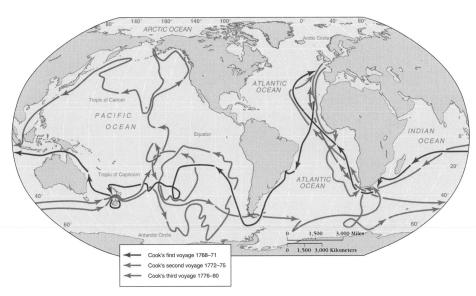

Figure 1.7   Voyages of Columbus and Magellan

Figure 1.8   Captain James Cook (1728–1779) and his voyages of exploration

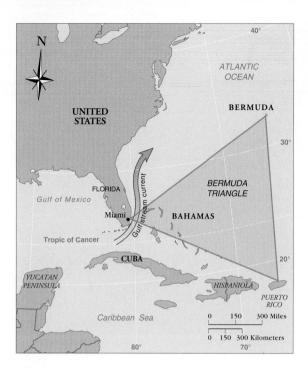

Figure 1F   Location map of the Bermuda Triangle

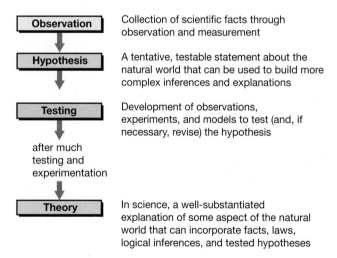

Observation	Collection of scientific facts through observation and measurement
Hypothesis	A tentative, testable statement about the natural world that can be used to build more complex inferences and explanations
Testing	Development of observations, experiments, and models to test (and, if necessary, revise) the hypothesis
after much testing and experimentation	
Theory	In science, a well-substantiated explanation of some aspect of the natural world that can incorporate facts, laws, logical inferences, and tested hypotheses

Figure 1.9   The scientific method

NOTES:

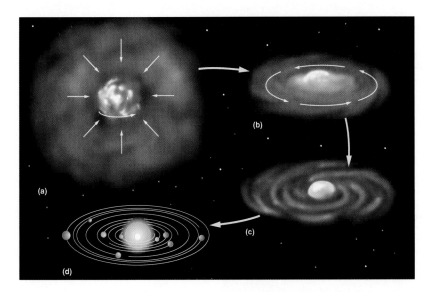

Figure 1.11   The nebular hypothesis

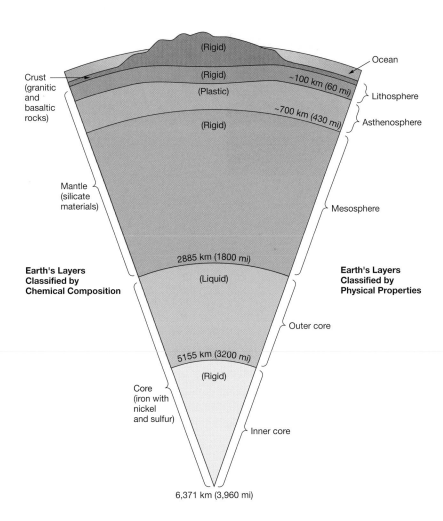

Figure 1.12   Comparison of Earth's chemical composition and physical properties

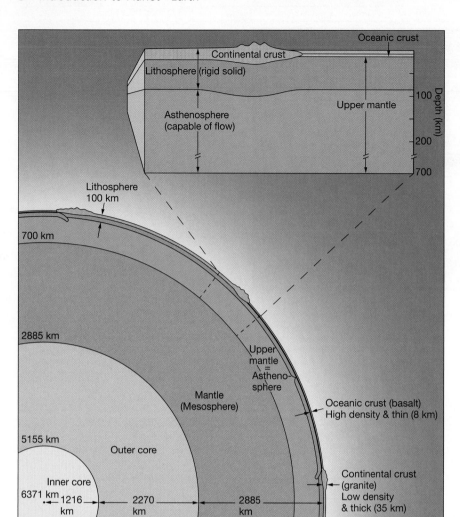

NOTES:

Figure 1.13   Internal structure of Earth

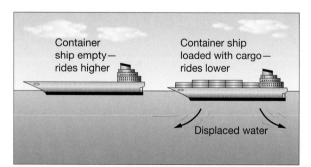

Figure 1.14   A container ship experiences isostatic adjustment

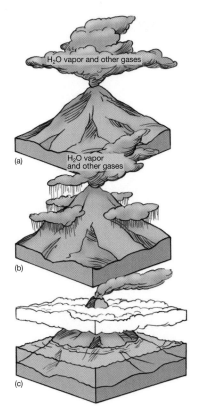

Figure 1.15   Formation of Earth's oceans

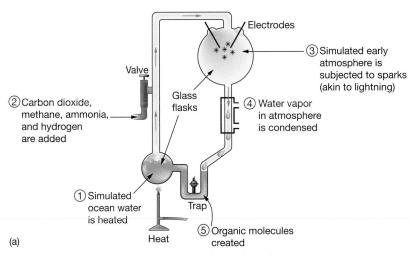

Figure 1.16   Creation of organic molecules

NOTES:

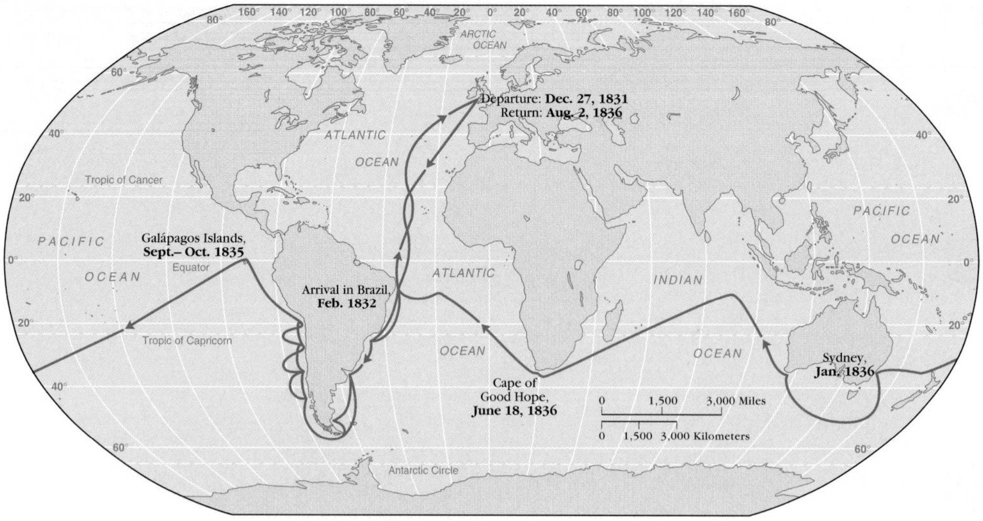

Figure 1G   Route of the HMS *Beagle*

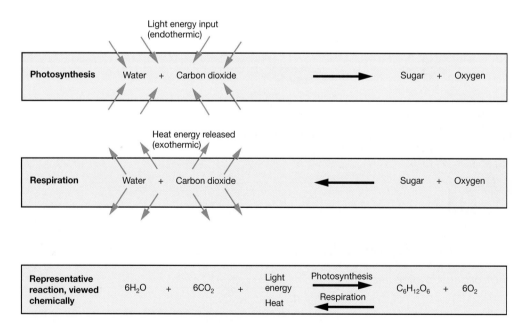

Figure 1.17   Photosynthesis, respiration, and representative reactions viewed chemically

NOTES:

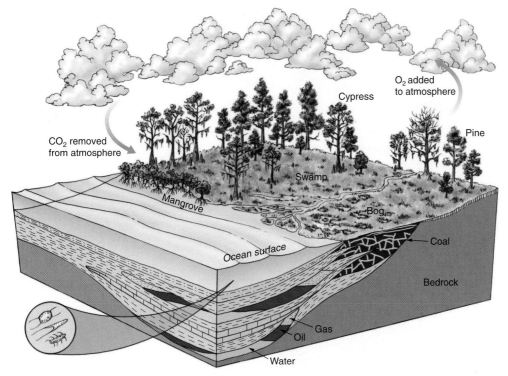

Figure 1.18   The effect of plants on Earth's environment

Uranium 235 atoms	1,000,000	500,000	250,000	125,000	62,500	31,250	15,625
Lead 207 atoms	0	500,000	750,000	875,000	937,500	968,750	984,375
Half-life (figures rounded for clarity)	**Zero** 4.2 billion years ago	**One** 3.5 billion years ago	**Two** 2.8 billion years ago	**Three** 2.1 billion years ago	**Four** 1.4 billion years ago	**Five** 700 million years ago	**Six** Today

Figure 1.19   Radiometric age dating

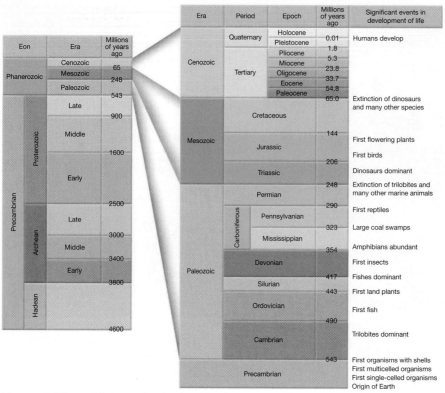

Era	Period	Epoch	Millions of years ago	Significant events in development of life
Cenozoic	Quaternary	Holocene	0.01	Humans develop
		Pleistocene	1.8	
	Tertiary	Pliocene	5.3	
		Miocene	23.8	
		Oligocene	33.7	
		Eocene	54.8	
		Paleocene	65.0	Extinction of dinosaurs and many other species
Mesozoic	Cretaceous		144	First flowering plants
	Jurassic		206	First birds
	Triassic		248	Dinosaurs dominant
Paleozoic	Permian		290	Extinction of trilobites and many other marine animals
	Carboniferous — Pennsylvanian		323	First reptiles
	Carboniferous — Mississippian		354	Large coal swamps
	Devonian		417	Amphibians abundant / First insects
	Silurian		443	Fishes dominant / First land plants
	Ordovician		490	First fish
	Cambrian		543	Trilobites dominant
Precambrian				First organisms with shells / First multicelled organisms / First single-celled organisms / Origin of Earth

Figure 1.20   The geologic time scale

NOTES:

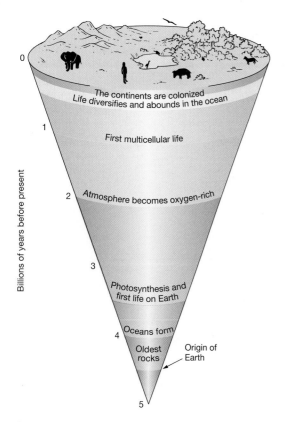

Figure 1H   A timeline of major events in Earth's development

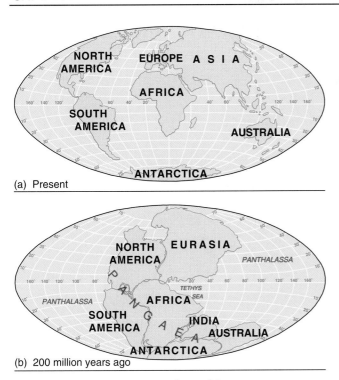

(a) Present

(b) 200 million years ago

Figure 2.2   Reconstruction of Pangaea

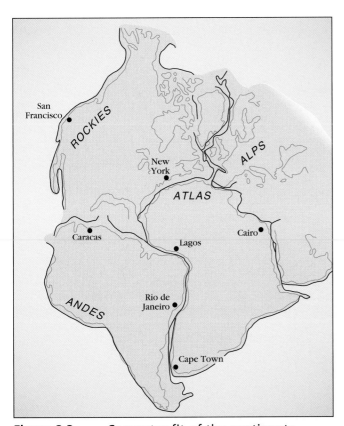

Figure 2.3   Computer fit of the continents

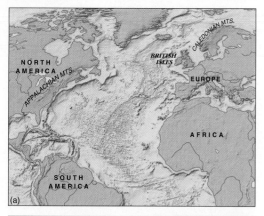

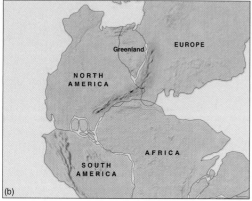

NOTES:

Figure 2.4   Matching mountain ranges across the North Atlantic Ocean

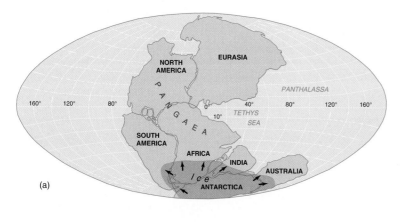

(a)

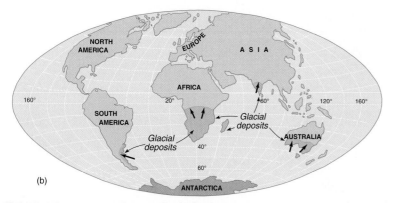

(b)

Figure 2.5   Ice age on Pangaea

NOTES:

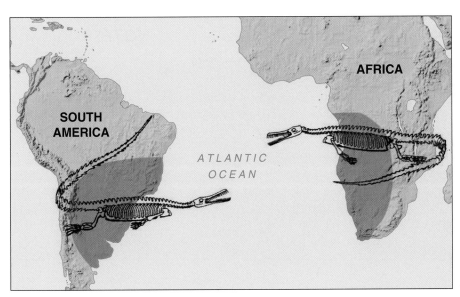

Figure 2.6   Fossils of *Mesosaurus*

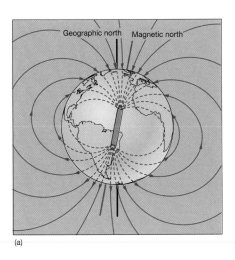

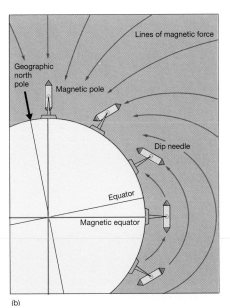

Figure 2.7   Earth's magnetic field

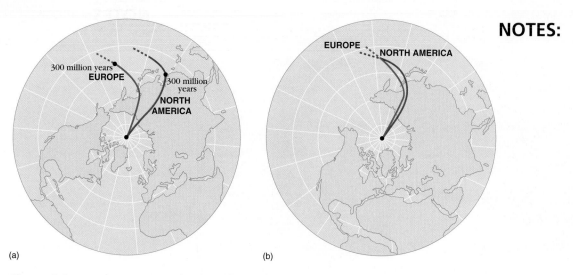

NOTES:

Figure 2.8   Apparent polar wandering paths

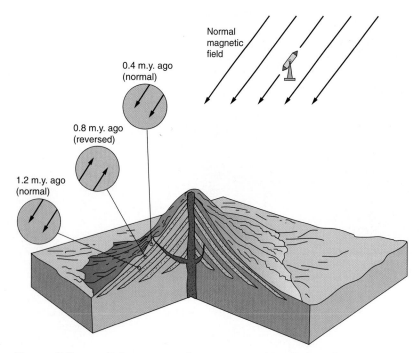

Figure 2.9   Paleomagnetism preserved in rocks

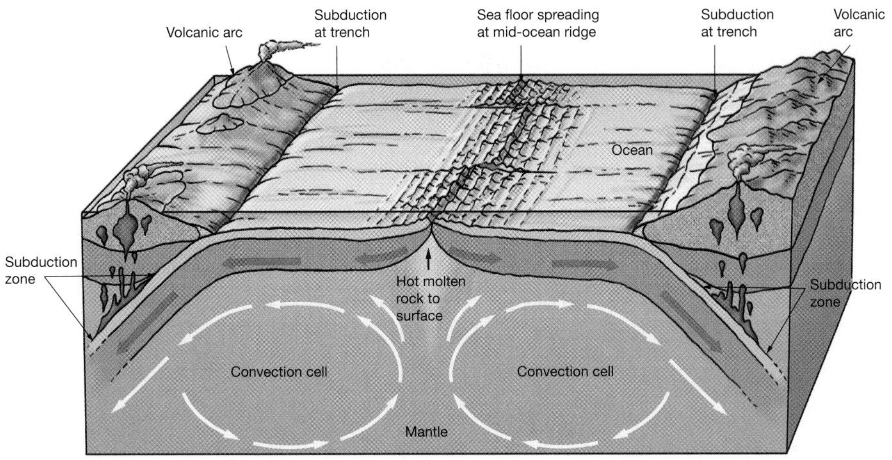

NOTES:

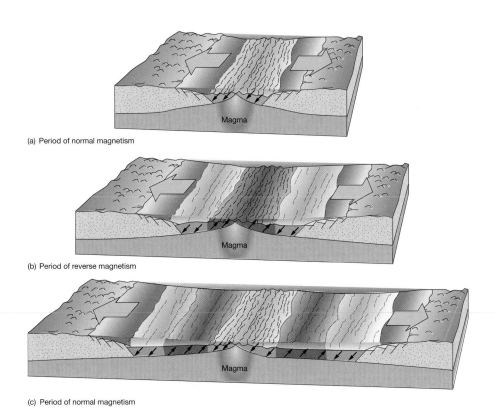

Figure 2.10   Processes of plate tectonics

(a) Period of normal magnetism

(b) Period of reverse magnetism

(c) Period of normal magnetism

Figure 2.11   Magnetic evidence of sea floor spreading

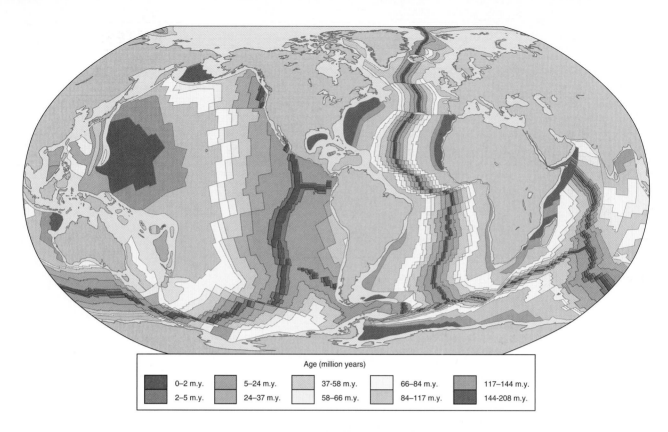

Figure 2.12 Age of the ocean crust beneath deep-sea deposits

NOTES:

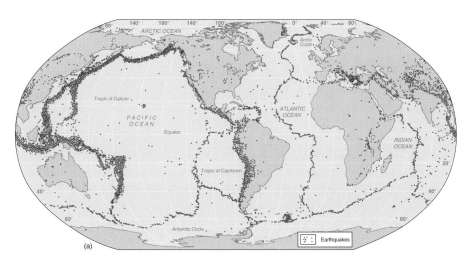

Figure 2.13a   Distribution of earthquakes

NOTES:

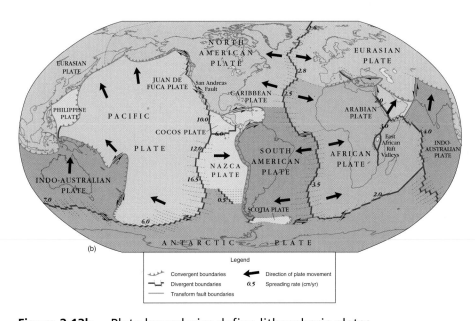

Figure 2.13b   Plate boundaries define lithospheric plates

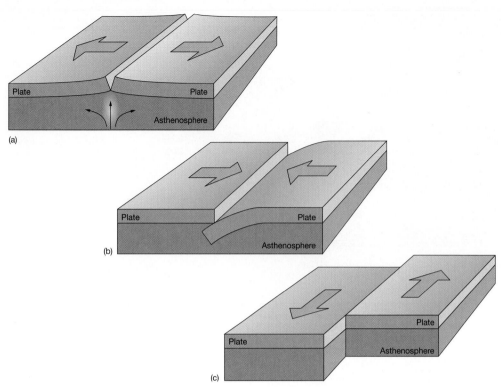

Figure 2.14 The three types of plate boundaries

NOTES:

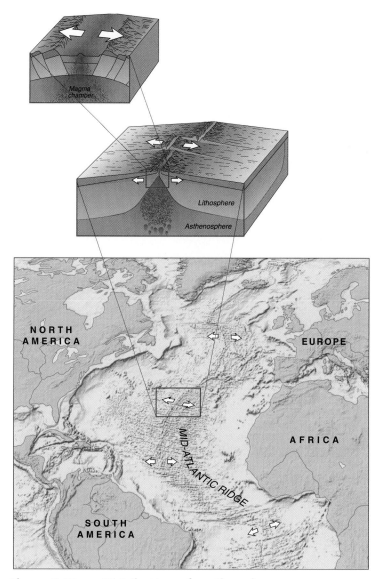

Figure 2.15   Distribution of earthquakes

NOTES:

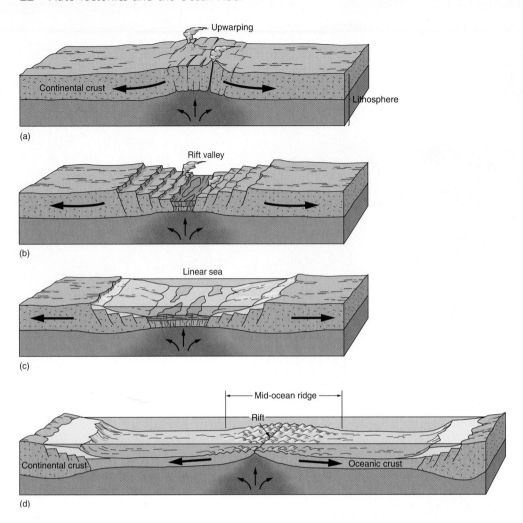

Upwarping

Continental crust

Lithosphere

(a)

Rift valley

(b)

Linear sea

(c)

Mid-ocean ridge

Rift

Continental crust

Oceanic crust

(d)

Figure 2.17   Formation of an ocean basin by sea floor spreading

NOTES:

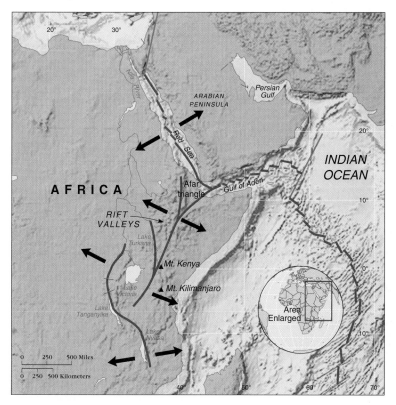

Figure 2.18   East African rift valleys and associated features

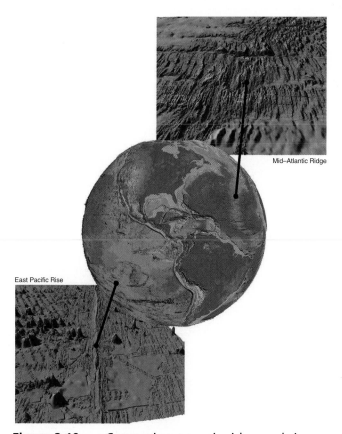

Figure 2.19   Comparing oceanic ridge and rises

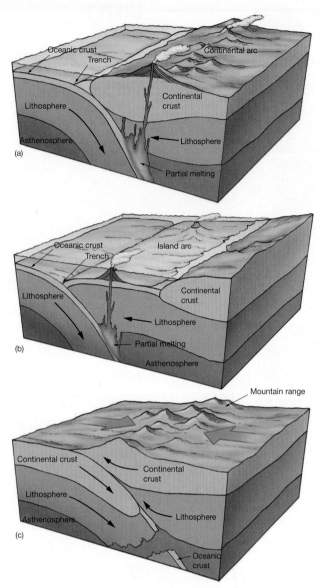

Figure 2.20   The three sub-types of convergent plate boundaries

NOTES:

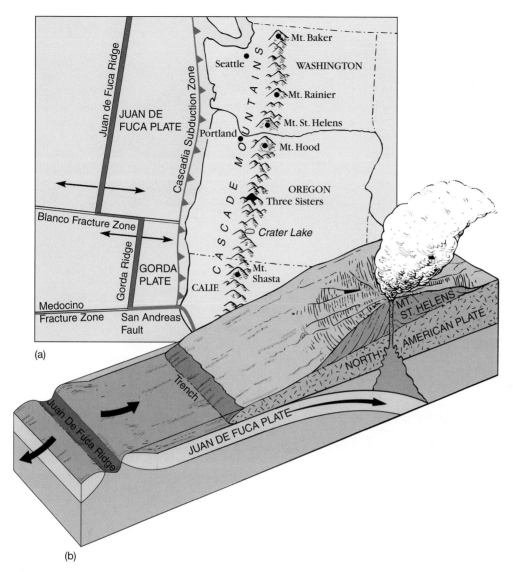

(a)

(b)

Figure 2.21   Convergent tectonic activity produces the Cascade Mountains

NOTES:

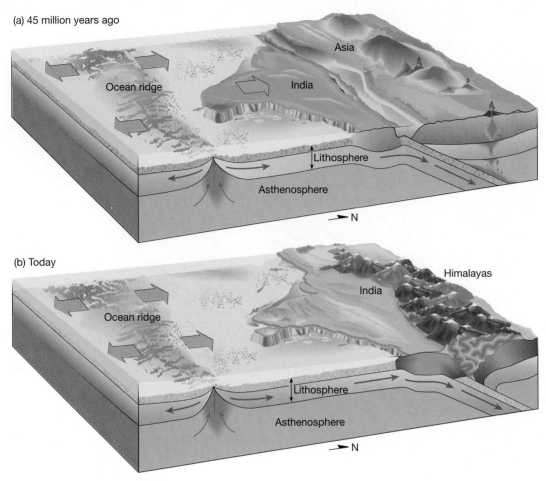

Figure 2.22 The collision of India with Asia

NOTES:

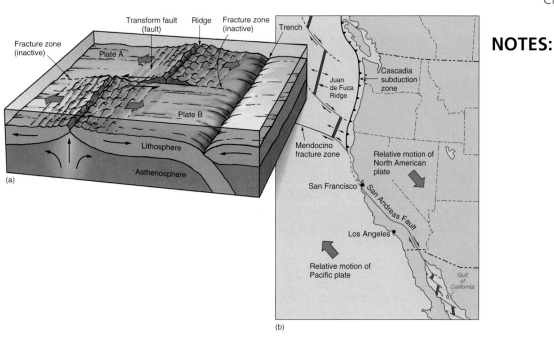

NOTES:

Figure 2.23   Transform faults

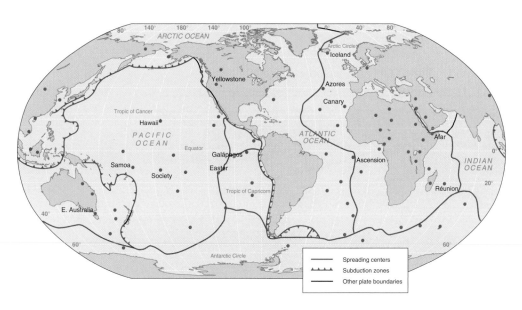

Figure 2.24   Global distribution of prominent hotspots

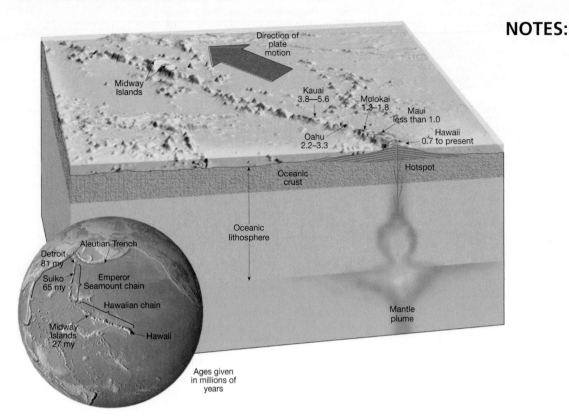

NOTES:

Figure 2.25 Hawaiian Islands-Emperor Seamount Chain

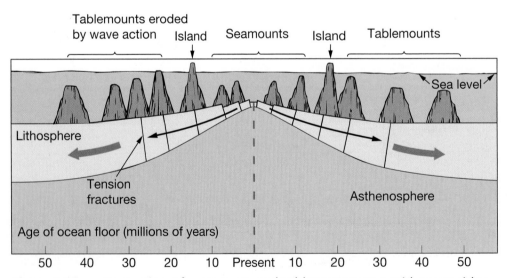

Figure 2.26 Formation of seamounts and tablemounts at a mid-ocean ridge

NOTES:

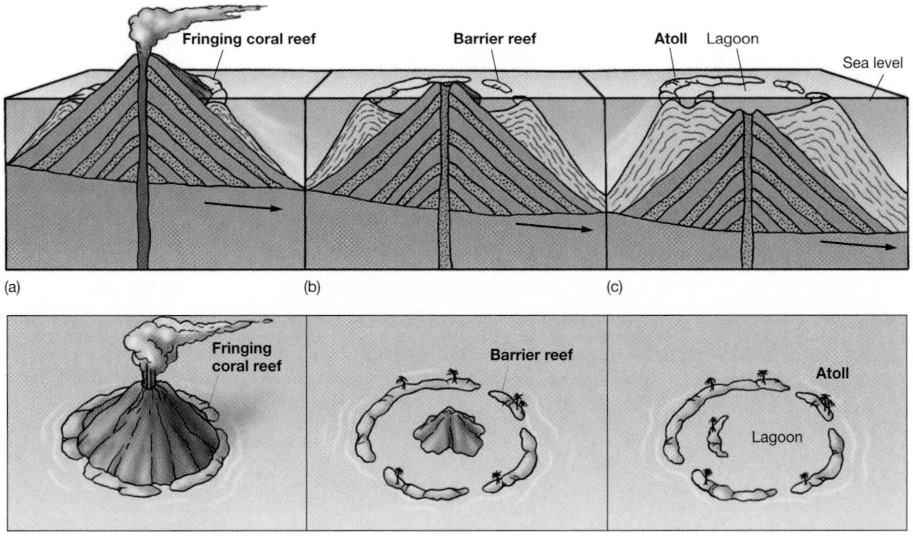

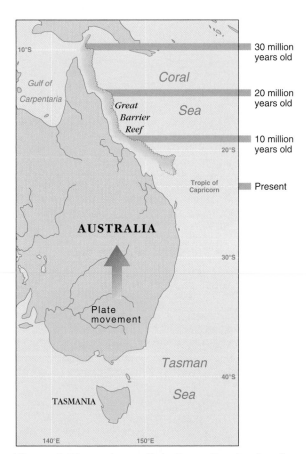

Figure 2.27 Stages of development in coral reefs

Figure 2.28 Australia's Great Barrier Reef as a recorder of plate movement

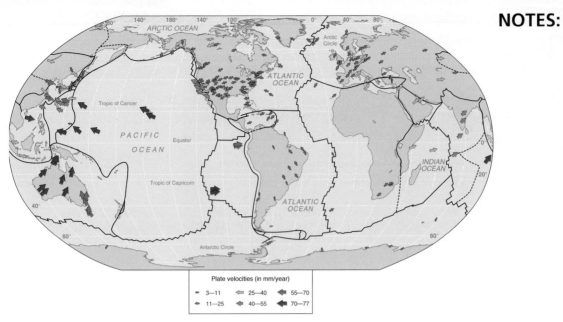

NOTES:

Figure 2.30   Satellite position of locations on Earth

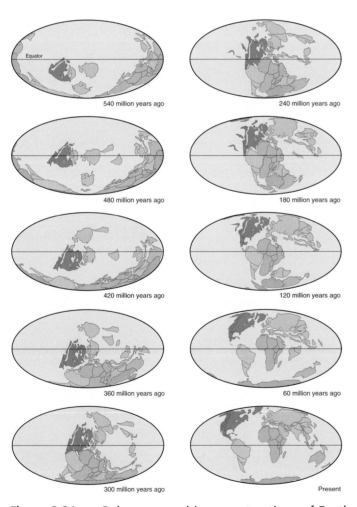

Figure 2.31   Paleogeographic reconstructions of Earth

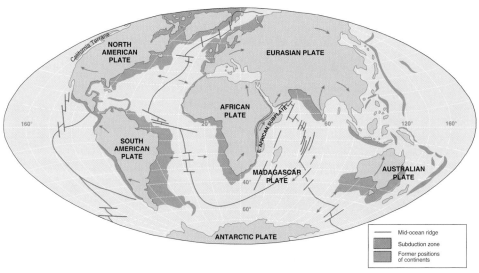

Figure 2.32   The world as it may look 50 million years from now

STAGE		MOTION	PHYSIOGRAPHY	EXAMPLE
EMBRYONIC		Uplift	Complex system of linear rift valleys on continent	East African rift valleys
JUVENILE		Divergence (spreading)	Narrow seas with matching coasts	Red Sea
MATURE		Divergence (spreading)	Ocean basin with continental margins	Atlantic and Arctic Oceans
DECLINING		Convergence (subduction)	Island arcs and trenches around basin edge	Pacific Ocean
TERMINAL		Convergence (collision) and uplift	Narrow, irregular seas with young mountains	Mediterranean Sea
SUTURING		Convergence and uplift	Young to mature mountain belts	Himalaya Mountains

Figure 2.33   The Wilson cycle of ocean basin evolution

NOTES:

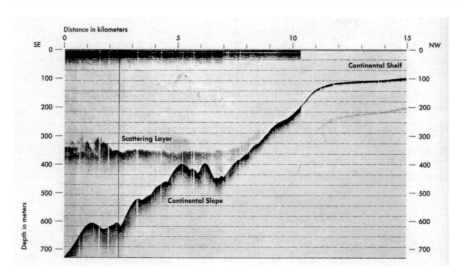

Figure 3.1   An echo sounder record

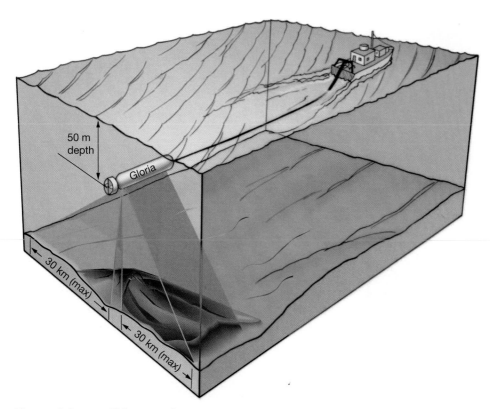

Figure 3.2   Side-scanning sonar

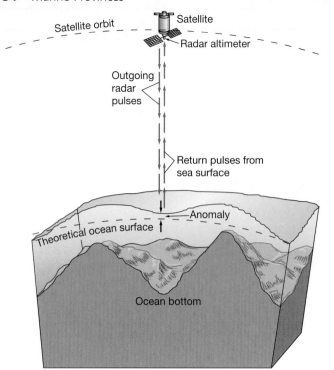

Figure 3A   Satellite measurements of the ocean surface

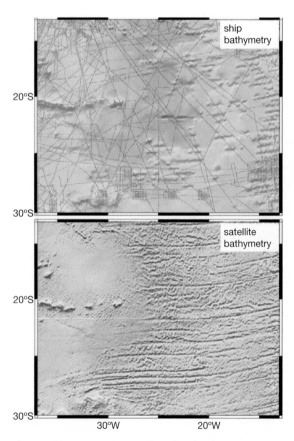

Figure 3B   Comparing bathymetric maps of the sea floor

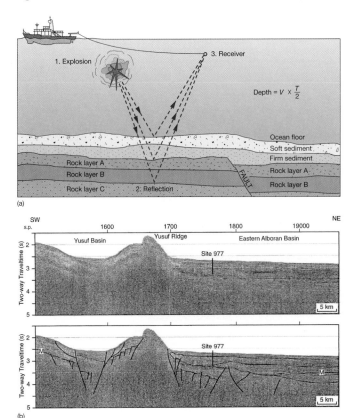

Figure 3C   Global sea surface elevation map from satellite data

Figure 3.3   Seismic profiling

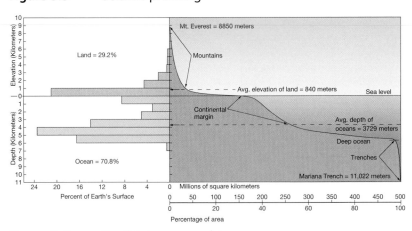

Figure 3.4   Earth's hypsographic curve

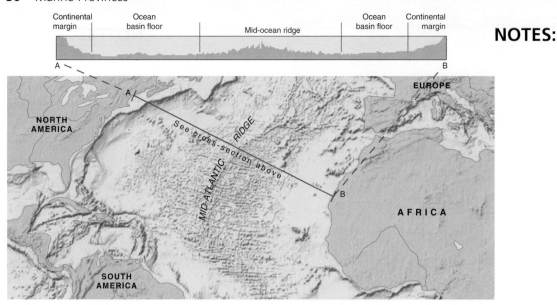

NOTES:

Figure 3.5   Major regions of the North Atlantic Ocean floor

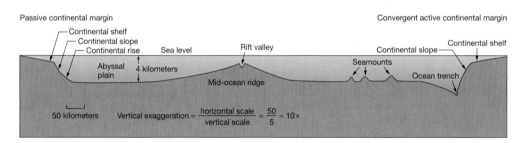

Figure 3.6   Passive and active continental margins

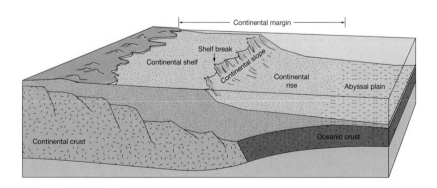

Figure 3.7   Features of a passive continental margin

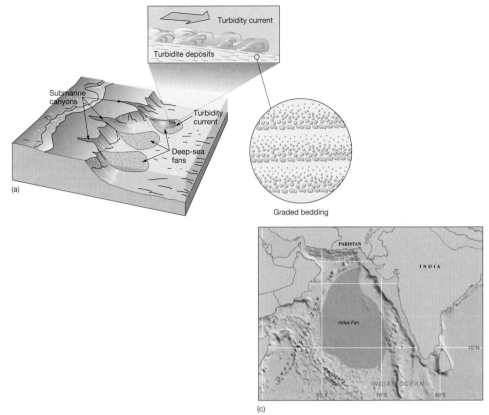

Figure 3.8   Submarine canyons and deep-sea fans

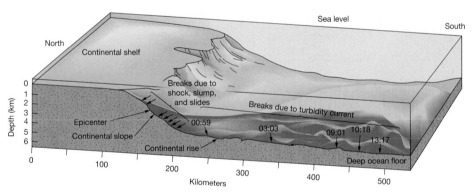

Figure 3E   Grand Banks earthquake

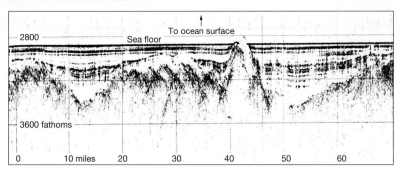

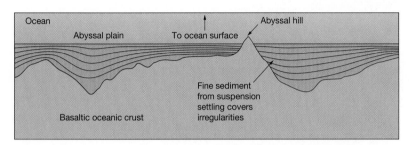

NOTES:

Figure 3.9 Abyssal plain formed by suspension settling

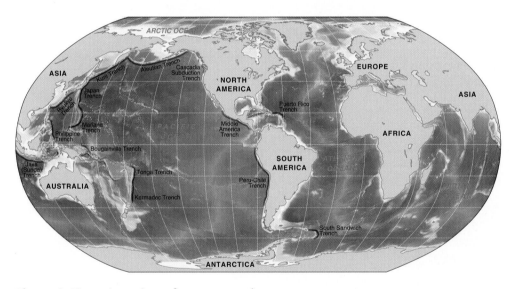

Figure 3.10 Location of ocean trenches

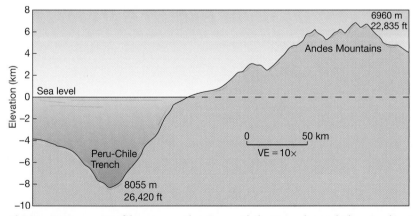

Figure 3.11 Profile across the Peru-Chile Trench and the Andes Mountains

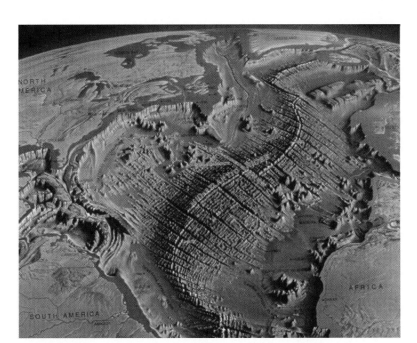

Figure 3.12   Floor of the North Atlantic Ocean

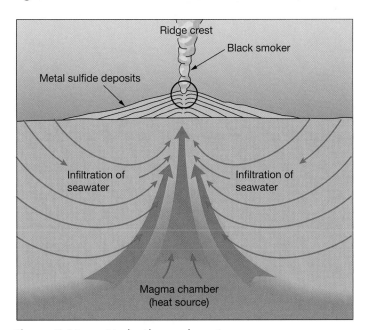

Figure 3.14   Hydrothermal vents

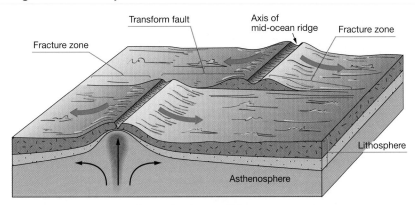

Figure 3.15   Transform faults and fracture zones

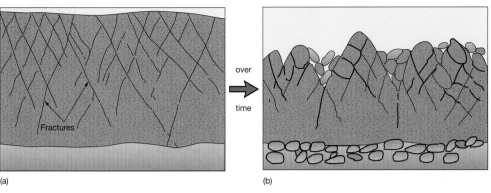

(a)   over   (b)
             time

Figure 4.3   Weathering

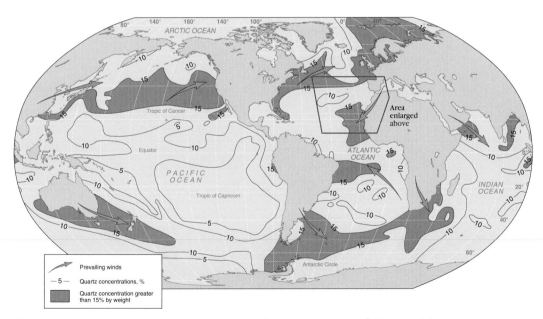

Figure 4.6   Lithogenous quartz in surface sediments of the world's oceans

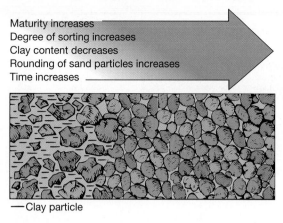

Maturity increases
Degree of sorting increases
Clay content decreases
Rounding of sand particles increases
Time increases

—Clay particle

Figure 4.7   Sediment maturity

NOTES:

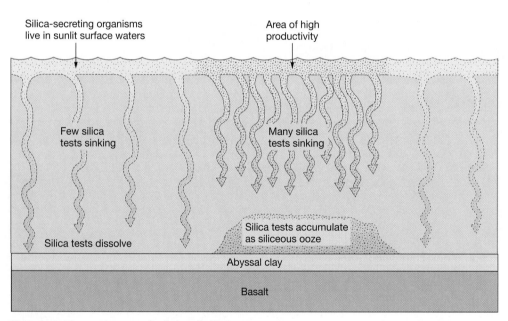

Silica-secreting organisms
live in sunlit surface waters

Area of high
productivity

Few silica
tests sinking

Many silica
tests sinking

Silica tests dissolve

Silica tests accumulate
as siliceous ooze

Abyssal clay

Basalt

Figure 4.12   Accumulation of siliceous ooze

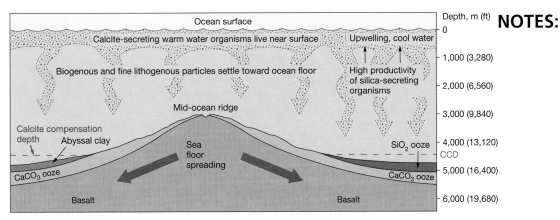

Figure 4.13   Sea floor spreading and sediment accumulation

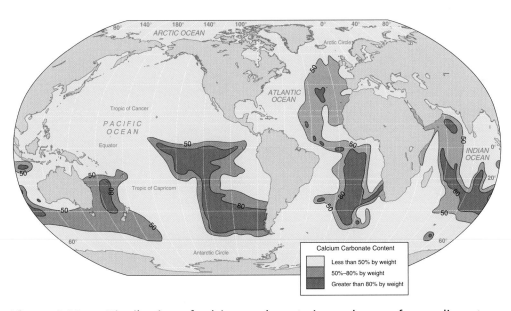

Figure 4.14   Distribution of calcium carbonate in modern surface sediments

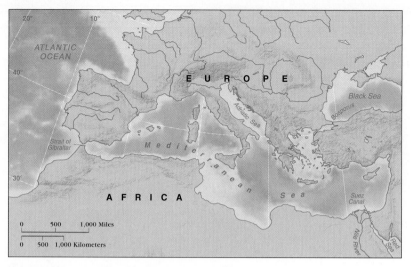

Figure 4B   The Mediterranean Sea

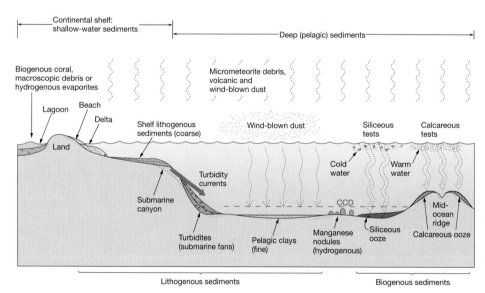

Figure 4.18   Distribution of sediment across a passive continental margin

NOTES:

NOTES:

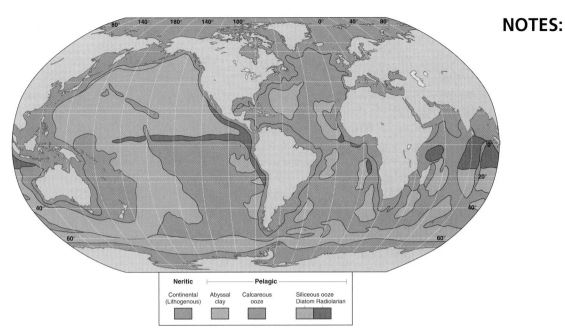

Figure 4.19   Distribution of neritic and pelagic sediments

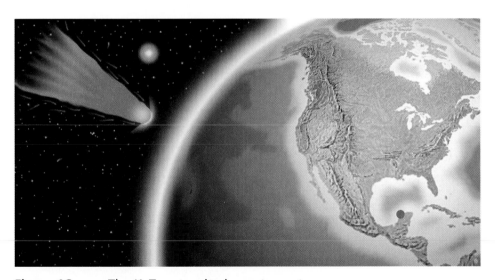

Figure 4C   The K–T meteorite impact event

Cretaceous/Tertiary Boundary meteorite impact
ODP Leg 171B, Site 1049, Core 1049A, Section 17X-2

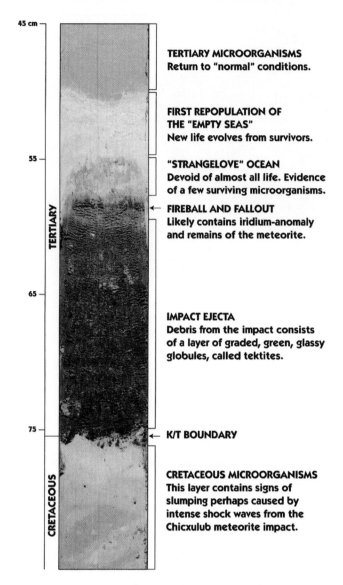

TERTIARY MICROORGANISMS
Return to "normal" conditions.

**FIRST REPOPULATION OF
THE "EMPTY SEAS"**
New life evolves from survivors.

"STRANGELOVE" OCEAN
Devoid of almost all life. Evidence
of a few surviving microorganisms.

FIREBALL AND FALLOUT
Likely contains iridium-anomaly
and remains of the meteorite.

IMPACT EJECTA
Debris from the impact consists
of a layer of graded, green, glassy
globules, called tektites.

K/T BOUNDARY

CRETACEOUS MICROORGANISMS
This layer contains signs of
slumping perhaps caused by
intense shock waves from the
Chicxulub meteorite impact.

Figure 4D   K–T boundary meteorite impact core

NOTES:

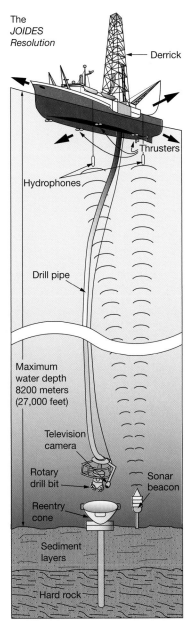

The
JOIDES
Resolution

Derrick

Thrusters

Hydrophones

Drill pipe

Maximum
water depth
8200 meters
(27,000 feet)

Television
camera

Rotary
drill bit

Sonar
beacon

Reentry
cone

Sediment
layers

Hard rock

Figure 4E   The drill ship *JOIDES* Resolution

NOTES:

NOTES:

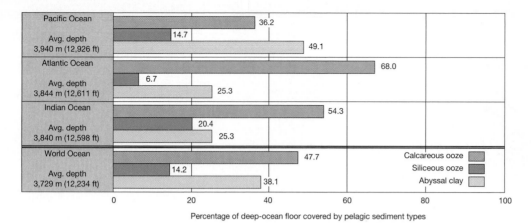

Figure 4.20 Percentage of pelagic sediment types within each ocean

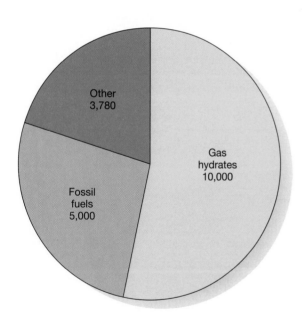

Figure 4.24 Organic carbon in Earth reservoirs

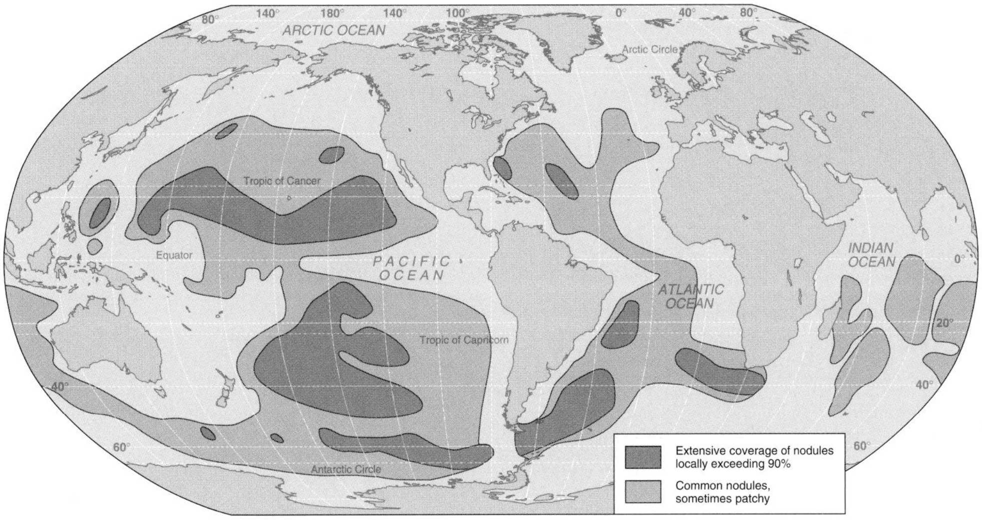

Figure 4.27   Distribution of manganese nodules on the sea floor

NOTES:

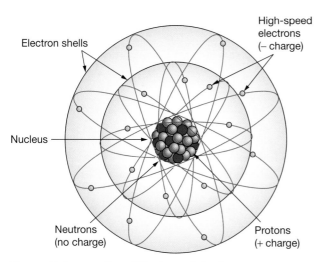

Figure 5.1   Simplified model of an atom

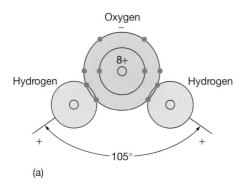

(a)

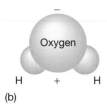

(b)

(c)

Figure 5.2   The water molecule

NOTES:

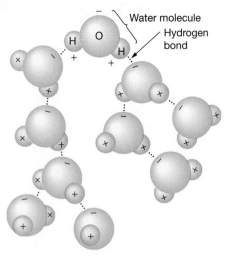

Figure 5.3   Hydrogen bonding in water

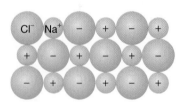

(a) Sodium chloride, solid crystal
    structure

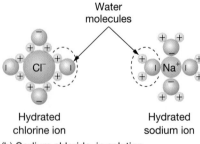

Hydrated   Hydrated
chlorine ion   sodium ion

(b) Sodium chloride, in solution

Figure 5.4   Water as a solvent

NOTES:

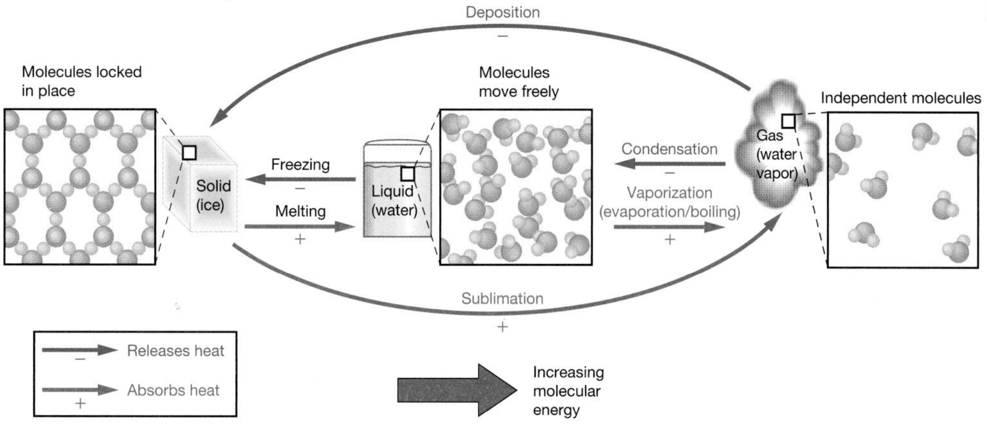

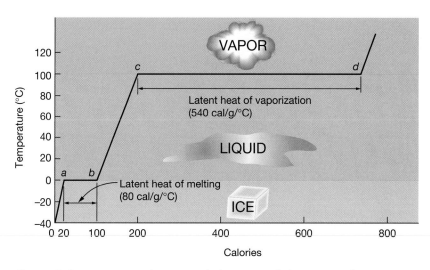

Figure 5.5   Water in the three states of matter

Figure 5.6   Latent heats and changes of the state of water

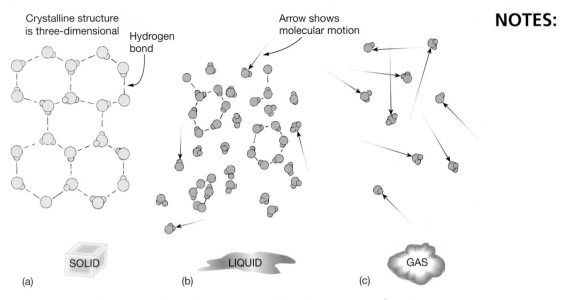

Figure 5.7 Hydrogen bonds in H₂O and the three states of matter

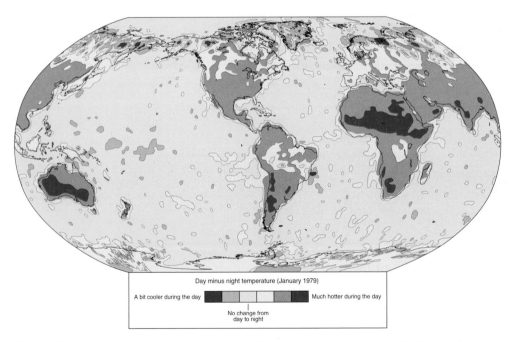

Figure 5.8 Atmospheric transport of surplus heat from low latitudes into heat-deficient high latitudes

NOTES:

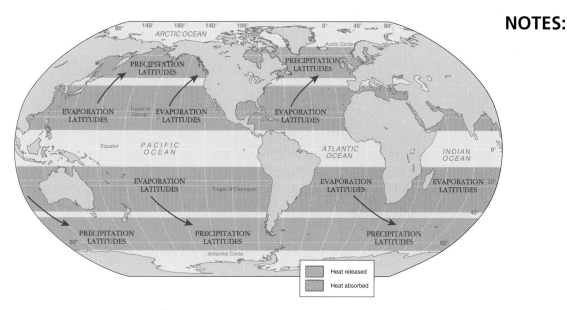

Figure 5.9   Day minus night temperature difference

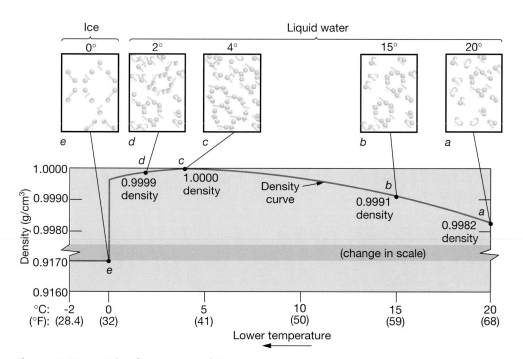

Figure 5.10   The formation of ice

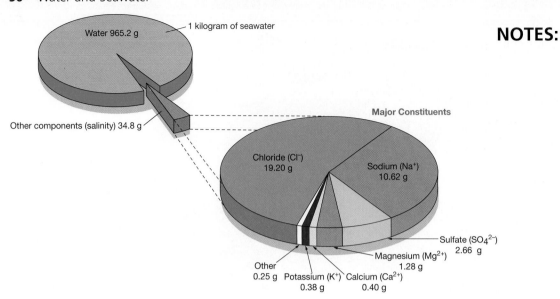

Figure 5.12   Major dissolved components in seawater

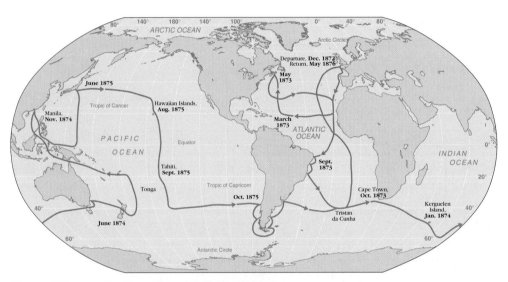

Figure 5B   Route of the HMS *Challenger*

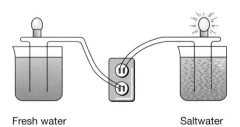

Figure 5.13   Affect of salinity on water conductivity

NOTES:

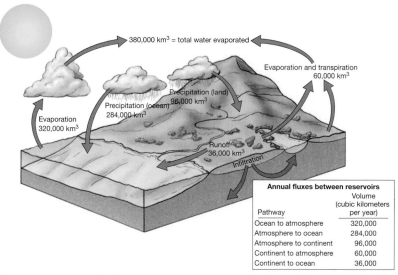

Figure 5.15   The hydrologic cycle

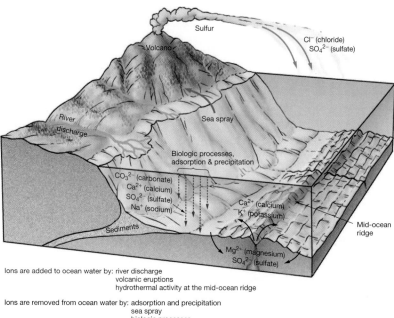

Figure 5.16   The cycling of dissolved components in seawater

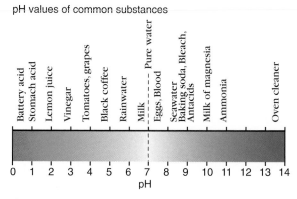

Figure 5.17   The pH scale

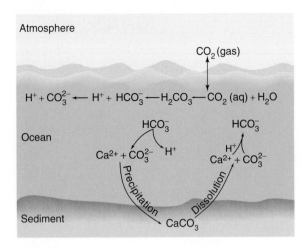

Seawater too basic: $H_2CO_3 \longrightarrow HCO_3^- + H^+$ pH drops
Seawater too acidic: $HCO_3^- + H^+ \longrightarrow H_2CO_3$ pH rises

Figure 5.18 The carbonate buffering system

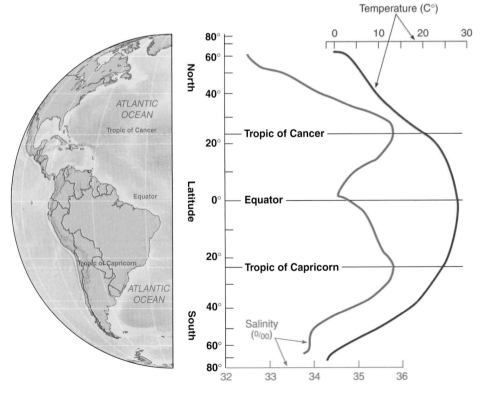

Figure 5.19 Surface salinity variation

NOTES:

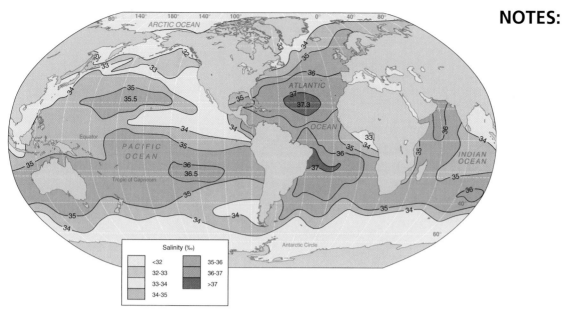

Figure 5.20   Average surface salinity of the oceans in August

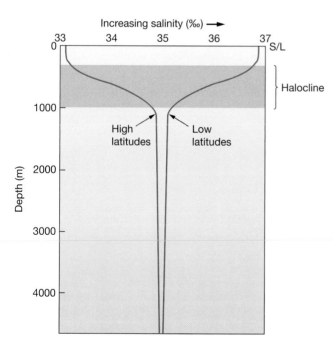

Figure 5.21   Salinity variation with depth

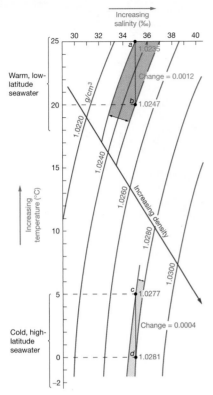

Figure 5.22   Seawater density variations with temperature and salinity

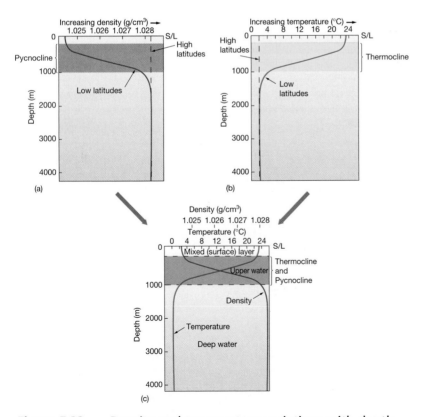

Figure 5.23   Density and temperature variations with depth

NOTES:

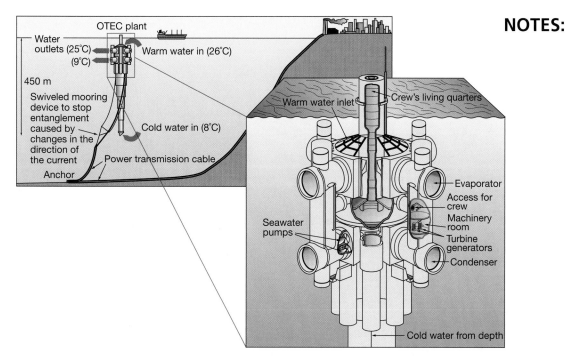

Figure 5C   Ocean Thermal Energy Conversion (OTEC)

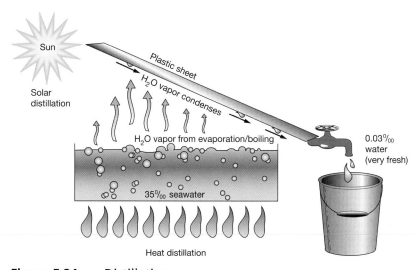

Figure 5.24   Distillation

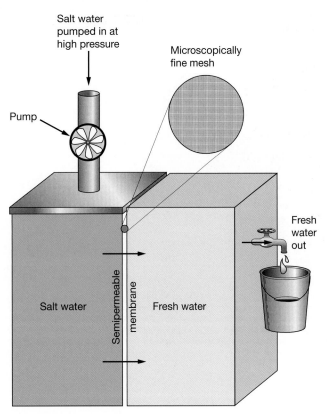

Salt water
pumped in at
high pressure

Microscopically
fine mesh

Pump

Fresh
water
out

Salt water

Semipermeable
membrane

Fresh water

Figure 5.25 Reverse osmosis

NOTES:

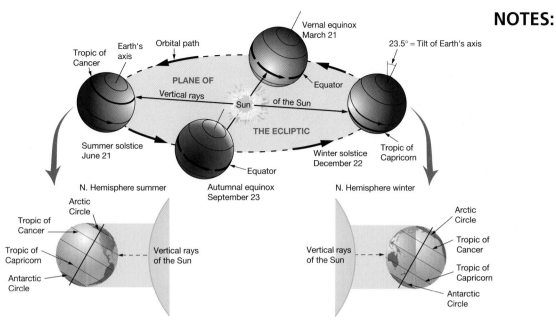

NOTES:

Figure 6.1   Earth's seasons

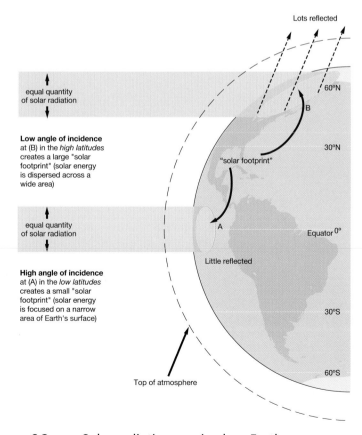

Figure 6.2   Solar radiation received on Earth

NOTES:

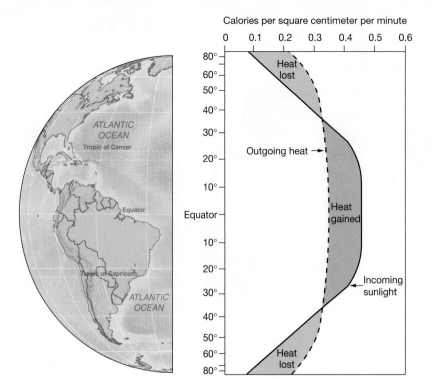

Figure 6.3   Heat gained and lost from the ocean varies with latitude

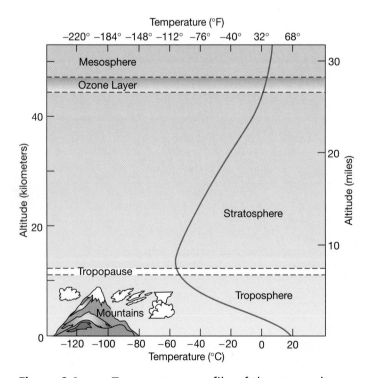

Figure 6.4   Temperature profile of the atmosphere

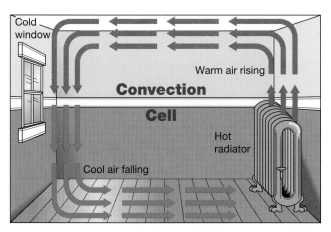

Figure 6.5   Convection in a room

NOTES:

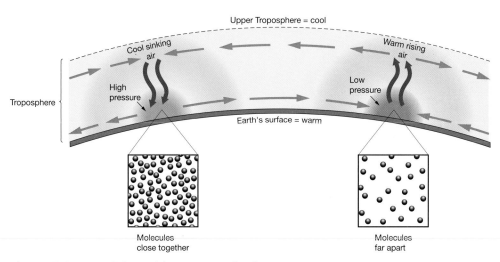

Figure 6.6   High and low atmospheric pressure zones

NOTES:

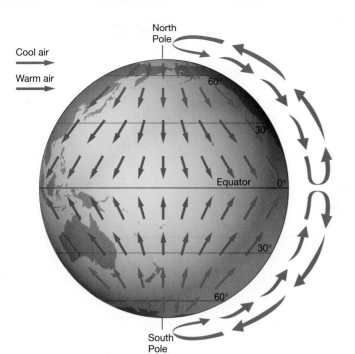

Figure 6.7   Atmospheric circulation on a nonspinning Earth

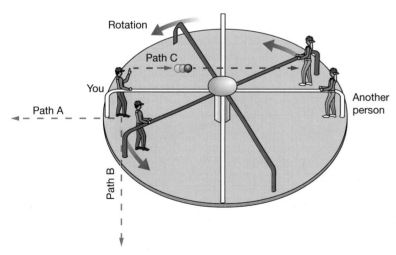

Figure 6.8   A merry-go-round spinning counterclockwise as viewed from above

NOTES:

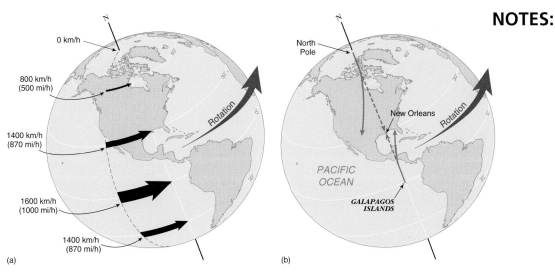

Figure 6.9   The Coriolis effect and missile paths

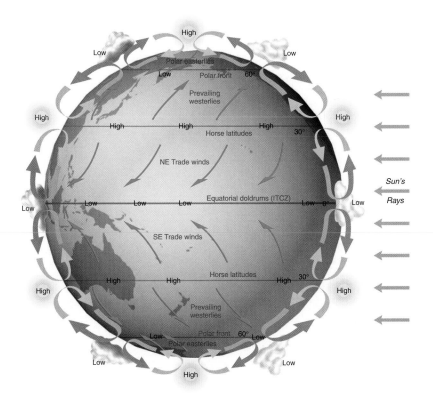

Figure 6.10   Atmospheric circulation and wind belts of the world

NOTES:

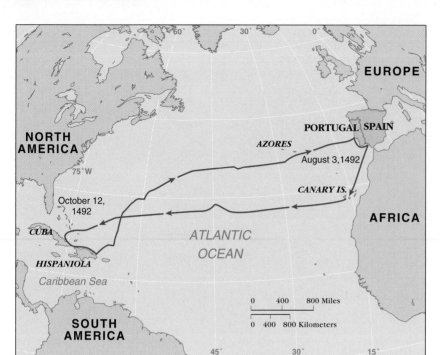

Figure 6A   Route of Christopher Columbus's first voyage

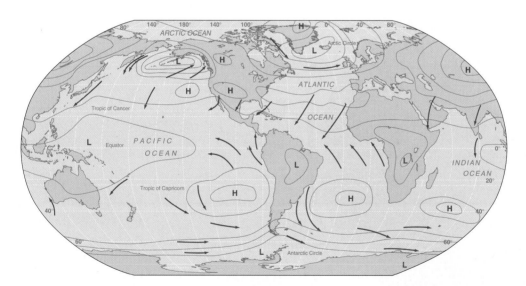

Figure 6.11   January sea-level atmospheric pressures and winds

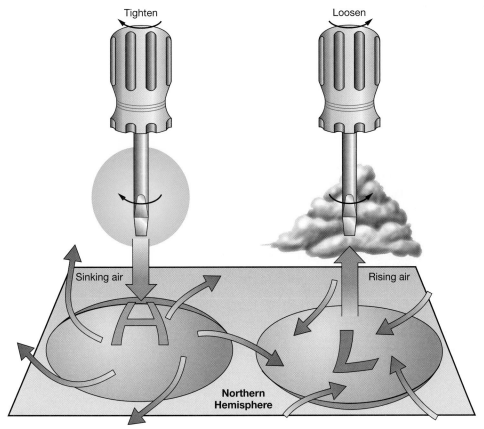

Figure 6.12   High-and low-pressure regions and air low

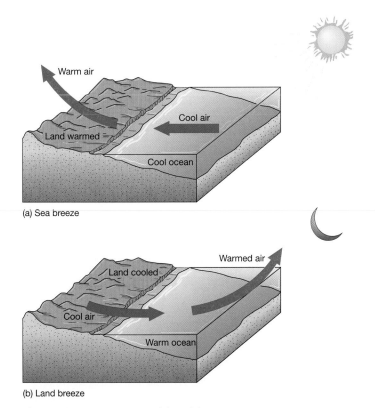

(a) Sea breeze

(b) Land breeze

Figure 6.13   Sea and land breezes

NOTES:

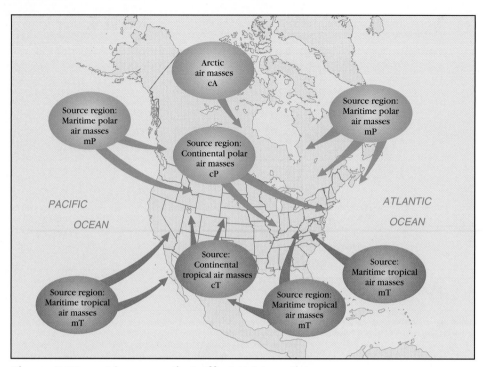

Figure 6.14   Air masses that affect U.S. weather

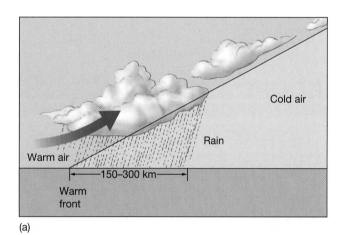

(a)

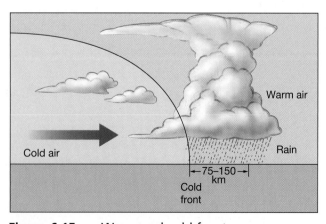

Figure 6.15   Warm and cold fronts

NOTES:

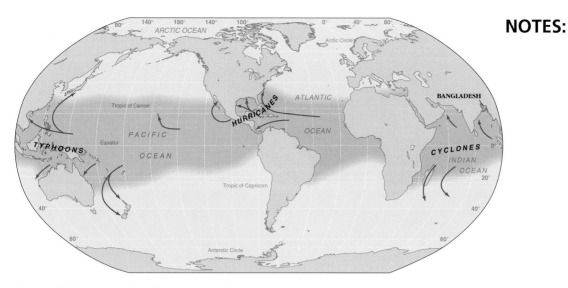

Figure 6.16   Paths of major tropical cyclones

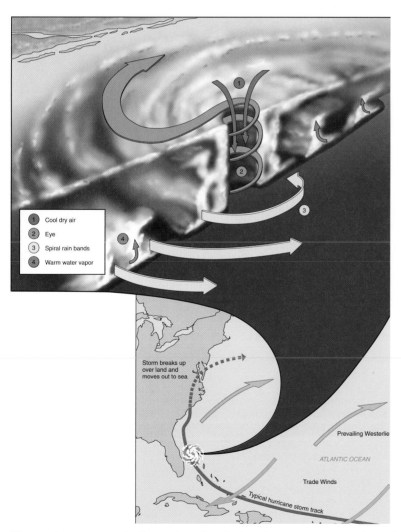

Figure 6.17   Typical North Atlantic hurricane storm track and internal structure

NOTES:

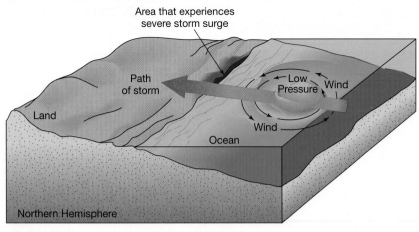

Figure 6.18   Storm surge

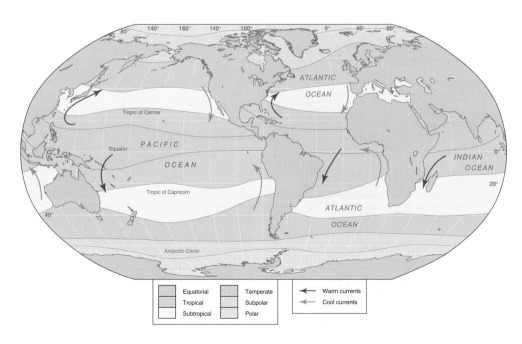

Figure 6.20   The ocean's climatic regions

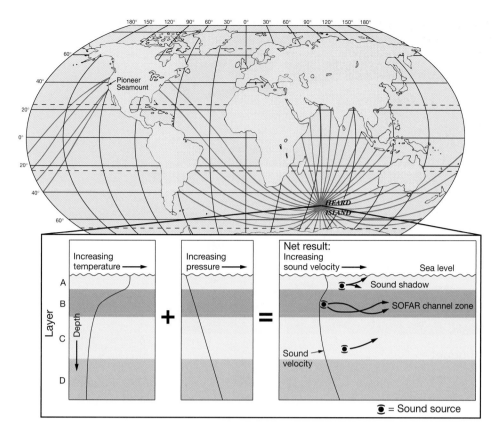

Figure 6D   The ATOC experiment

Figure 6.23   How a greenhouse works

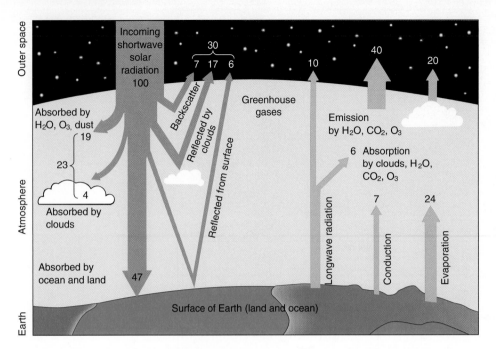

Figure 6.24   Earth's heat budget

NOTES:

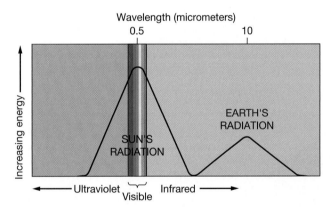

Figure 6.25   Energy radiated by the Sun and Earth

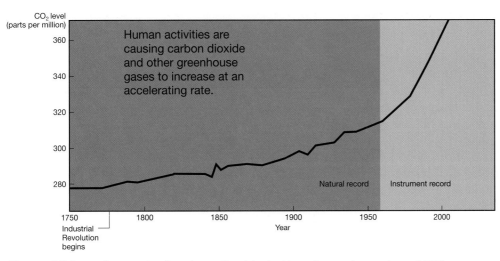

Figure 6.26   Amount of carbon dioxide in the atmosphere since 1750

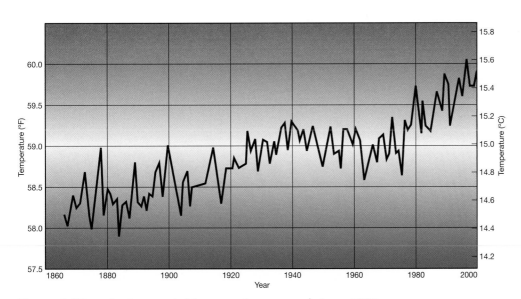

Figure 6.27   Instrumental temperature record since 1865

NOTES:

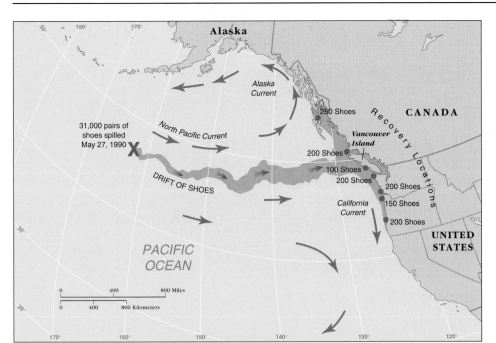

Figure 7A   Path of drifting shoes and recovery locations from the 1990 spill; recovered shoes and plastic bathtub toys

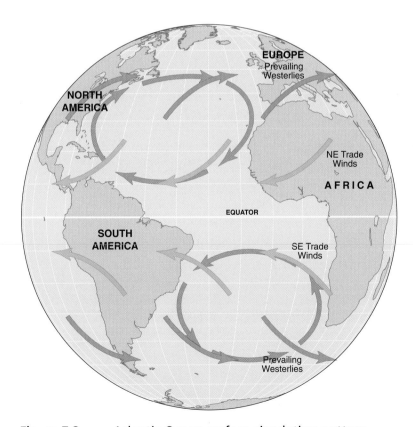

Figure 7.3   Atlantic Ocean surface circulation pattern

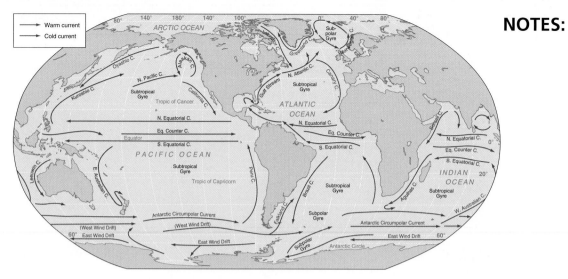

NOTES:

Figure 7.4   Wind-driven surface currents

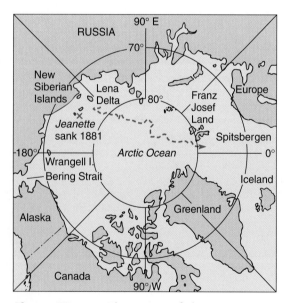

Figure 7B   The route of the *Fram*

NOTES:

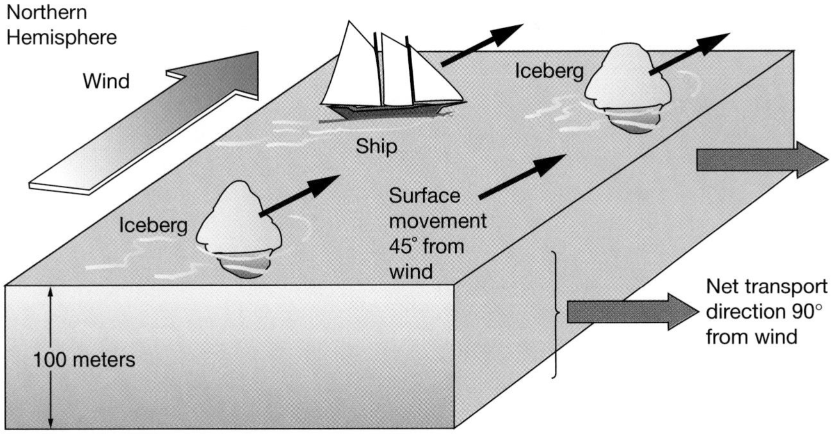

Northern
Hemisphere

Wind

Iceberg

Ship

Iceberg

Surface
movement
45° from
wind

Net transport
direction 90°
from wind

100 meters

Figure 7.5   Transport of floating objects

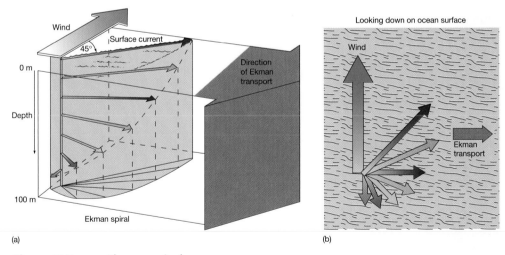

Wind

45°

Surface current

Direction
of Ekman
transport

0 m

Depth

100 m

Ekman spiral

(a)

Looking down on ocean surface

Wind

Ekman
transport

(b)

Figure 7.6   Ekman spiral

NOTES:

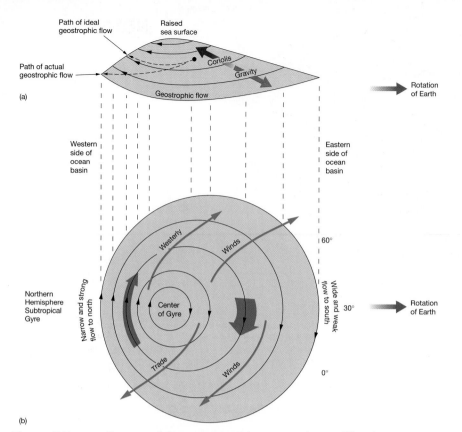

Figure 7.7   Geostrophic current and western intensification

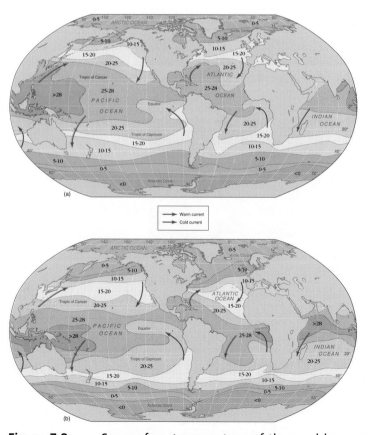

Figure 7.8   Sea surface temperature of the world ocean

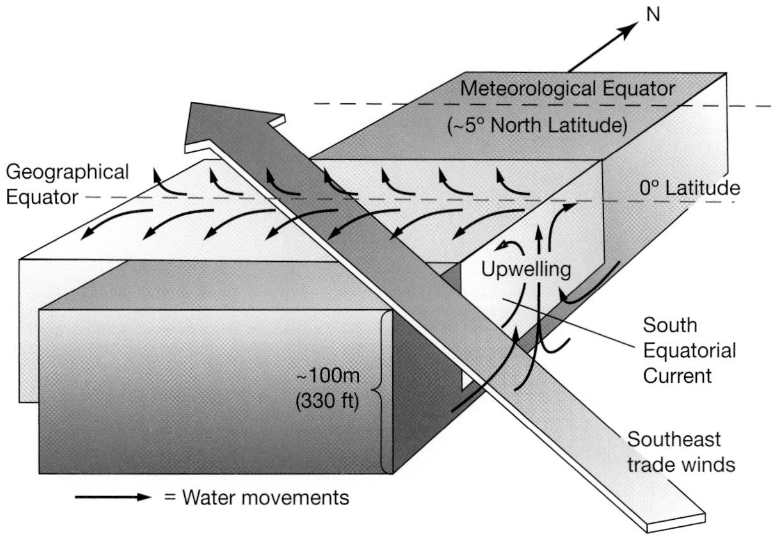

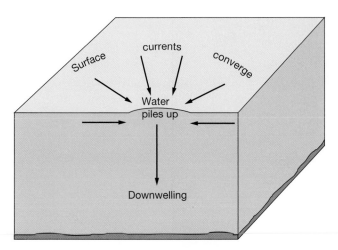

N

Meteorological Equator
(~5° North Latitude)

Geographical
Equator

0° Latitude

Upwelling

South
Equatorial
Current

Southeast
trade winds

~100m
(330 ft)

⟶ = Water movements

Figure 7.9   Equatorial upwelling

Surface   currents   converge

Water
piles up

Downwelling

Figure 7.10   Downwelling caused by convergence of surface currents

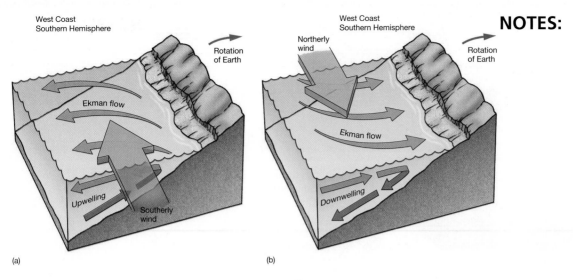

NOTES:

Figure 7.11 Coastal upwelling and downwelling

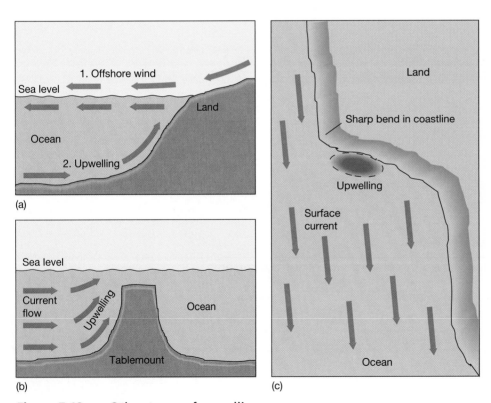

Figure 7.12 Other types of upwelling

NOTES:

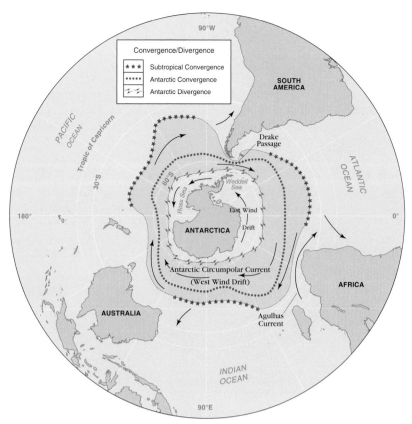

Figure 7.13   Antarctic surface circulation

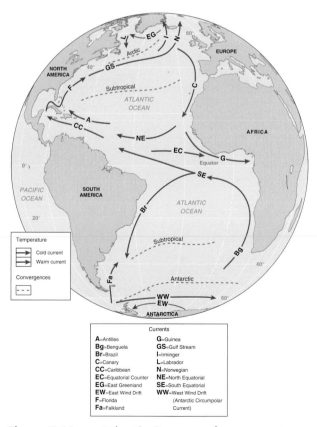

Figure 7.14   Atlantic Ocean surface currents

NOTES:

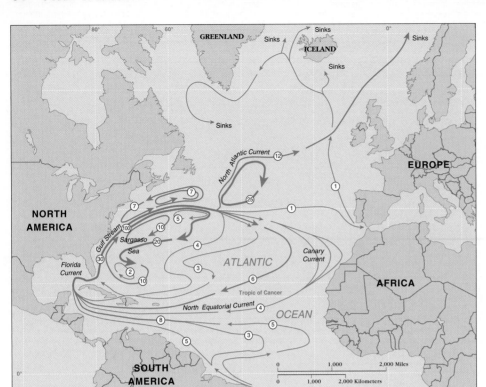

Figure 7.15   North Atlantic Ocean circulation

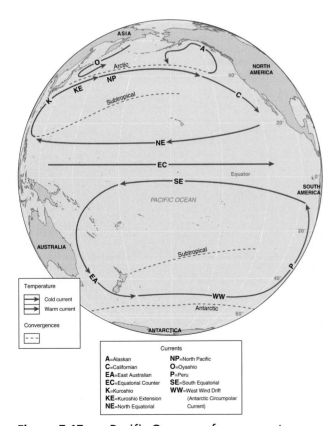

Figure 7.17   Pacific Ocean surface currents

NOTES:

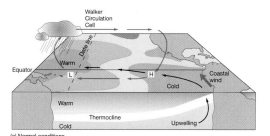

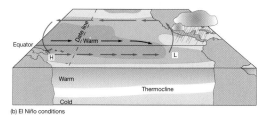

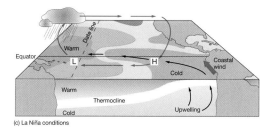

(a) Normal conditions

(b) El Niño conditions

(c) La Niña conditions

Figure 7.18   Normal, El Niño, and La Niña conditions

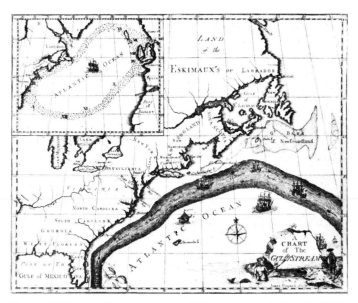

Figure 7C   Benjamin Franklin's chart of the Gulf Stream

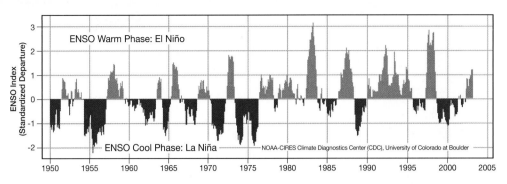

Figure 7.20   Multivariate ENSO index 1950-present

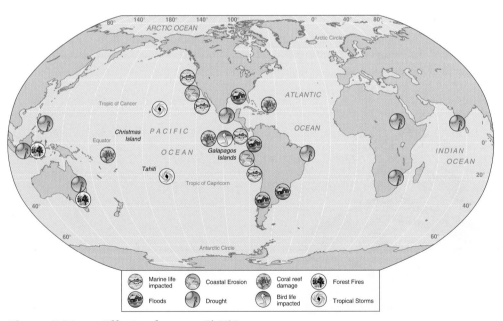

Figure 7.21   Effects of severe El Niños

NOTES:

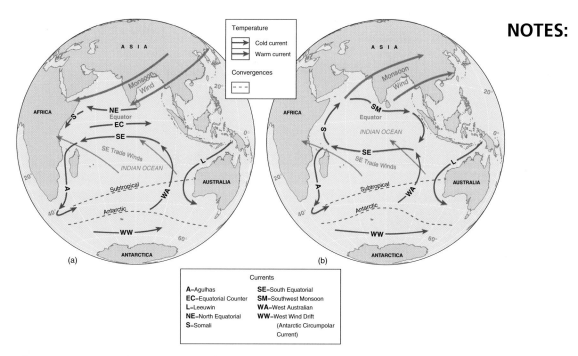

Figure 7.23   Indian Ocean surface currents

Currents

A=Agulhas SE=South Equatorial
EC=Equatorial Counter SM=Southwest Monsoon
L=Leeuwin WA=West Australian
NE=North Equatorial WW=West Wind Drift
S=Somali (Antarctic Circumpolar Current)

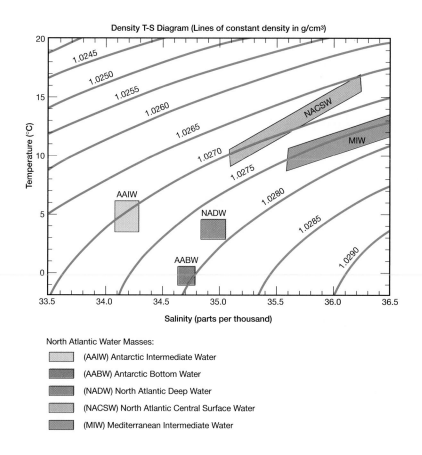

North Atlantic Water Masses:

- (AAIW) Antarctic Intermediate Water
- (AABW) Antarctic Bottom Water
- (NADW) North Atlantic Deep Water
- (NACSW) North Atlantic Central Surface Water
- (MIW) Mediterranean Intermediate Water

Figure 7.24   Temperature-Salinity (T-S) diagram

NOTES:

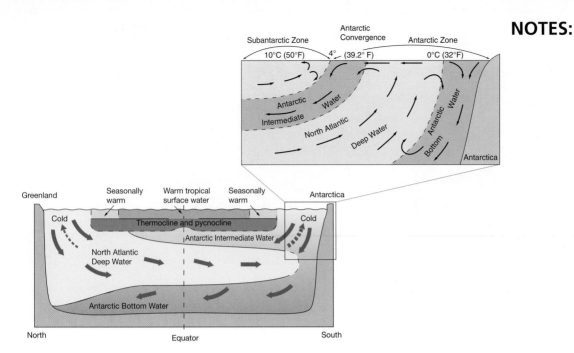

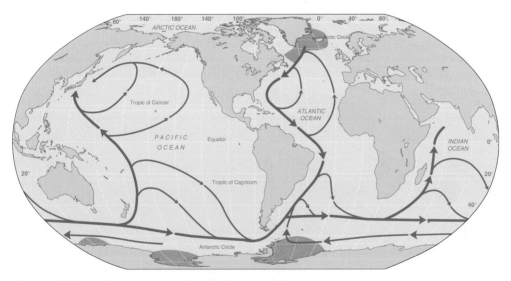

Figure 7.25   Atlantic Ocean subsurface water masses

Figure 7.26   Deep-water circulation model

NOTES:

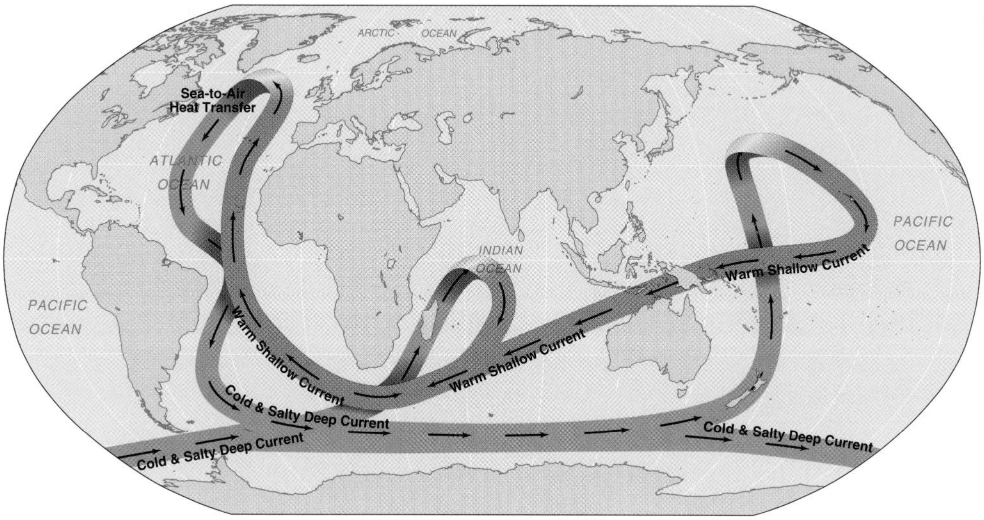

Figure 7.27 Conveyer-belt circulation

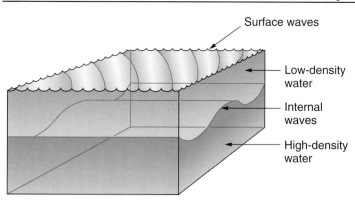

Surface waves

Low-density water

Internal waves

High-density water

Figure 8.1   Internal waves

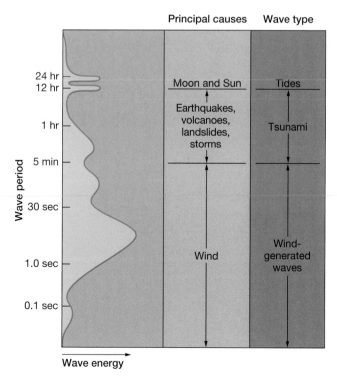

Principal causes   Wave type

Wave period

24 hr
12 hr   Moon and Sun   Tides

                Earthquakes,
                volcanoes,
1 hr   landslides,   Tsunami
                storms

5 min

30 sec

                                        Wind-
1.0 sec   Wind   generated
                                        waves

0.1 sec

Wave energy

Figure 8.2   Distribution of energy in ocean waves

NOTES:

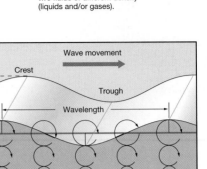

LONGITUDINAL WAVE
Particles (color) move back and forth in direction of energy transmission. These waves transmit energy through all states of matter.

TRANSVERSE WAVE
Particles (color) move back and forth at right angles to direction of energy transmission. These waves transmit energy only through solids.

ORBITAL WAVE
Particles (color) move in orbital path. These waves transmit energy along interface between two fluids of different density (liquids and/or gases).

(a) Types of progressive waves

(b) Wave characteristics

Figure 8.3   Types and characteristics of progressive waves

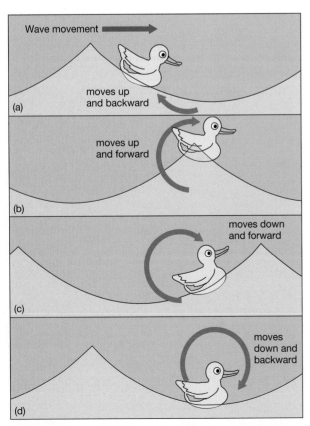

Figure 8.4   A floating rubber ducky shows circular orbital motion

Wave movement ➡️

NOTES:

1/2 wavelength

|◄——————— 1 wavelength ———————►|

Still water level

Depth = 1/2 wavelength

Wave base

Negligible water movement due to waves below wave base

Figure 8.5   Orbital motion in waves

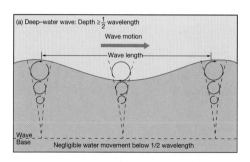

(a) Deep–water wave: Depth ≥ $\frac{1}{2}$ wavelength

Wave motion

Wave length

Wave Base   Negligible water movement below 1/2 wavelength

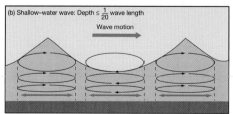

(b) Shallow–water wave: Depth ≤ $\frac{1}{20}$ wave length

Wave motion

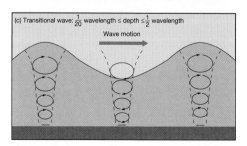

(c) Transitional wave: $\frac{1}{20}$ wavelength ≤ depth ≤ $\frac{1}{2}$ wavelength

Wave motion

Figure 8.6   Characteristics of deep-water, shallow-water, and transitional waves

NOTES:

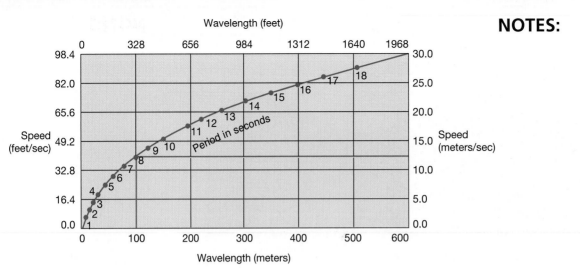

Figure 8.7 Speed of deep-water waves

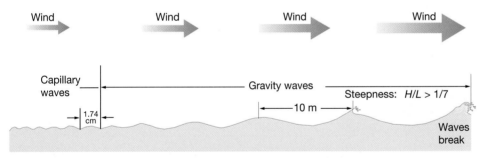

Figure 8.8 Wind creates capillary and gravity waves

NOTES:

Figure 8.9   The "sea" and swell

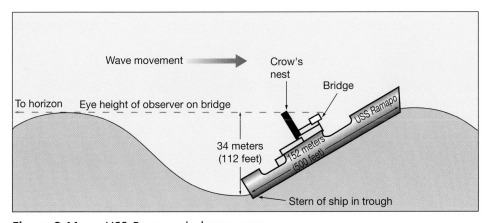

Figure 8.11   USS *Ramapo* in heavy seas

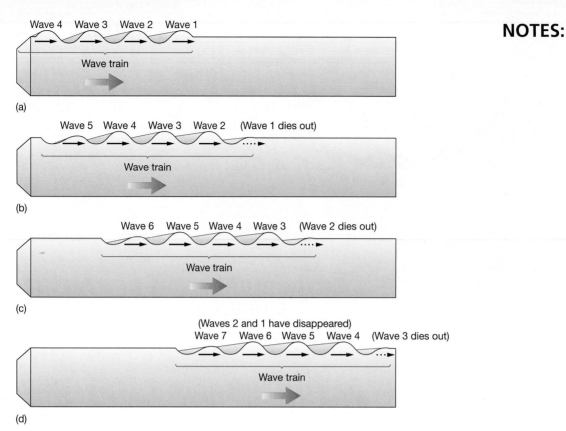

NOTES:

Figure 8.13   Movement of a wave train

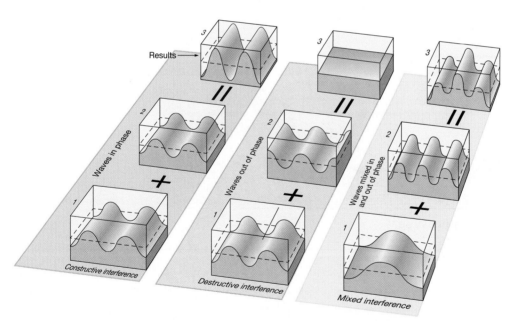

Figure 8.14   Constructive, destructive, and mixed interference patterns

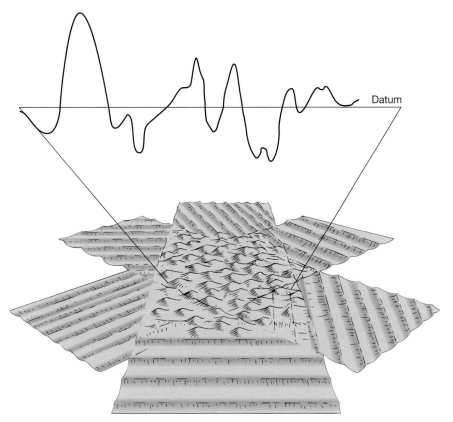

Figure 8.15   Mixed interference pattern

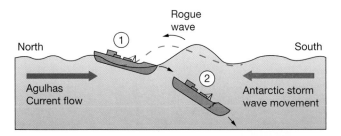

Figure 8A   Rogue waves along Africa's "Wild Coast"

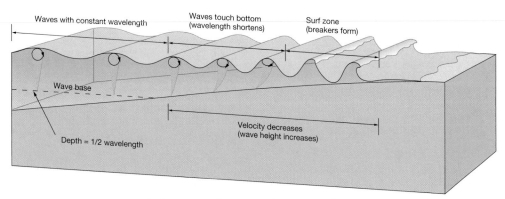

Figure 8.16   Physical changes of a wave in the surf zone

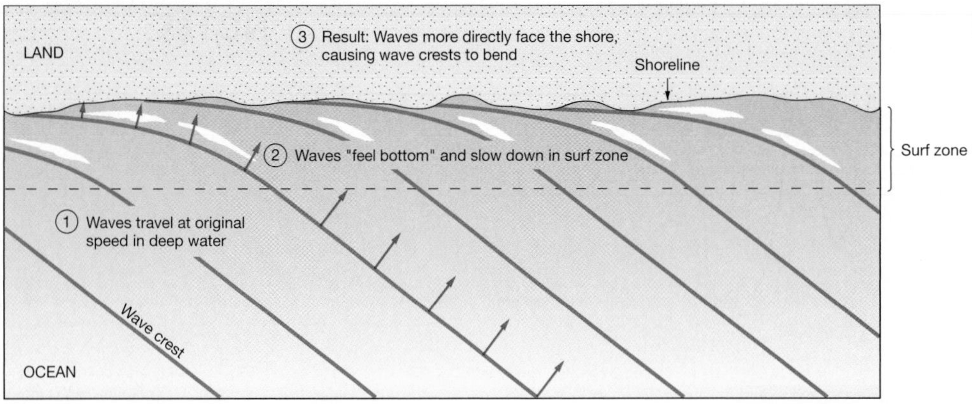

NOTES:

LAND

③ Result: Waves more directly face the shore, causing wave crests to bend

Shoreline

② Waves "feel bottom" and slow down in surf zone

Surf zone

① Waves travel at original speed in deep water

Wave crest

OCEAN

(a)

Figure 8.18a Wave refraction: straight shoreline

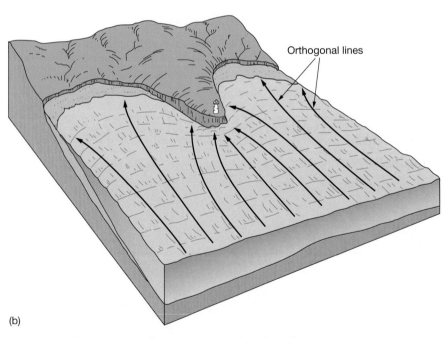

Orthogonal lines

(b)

Figure 8.18b Wave refraction: irregular shoreline

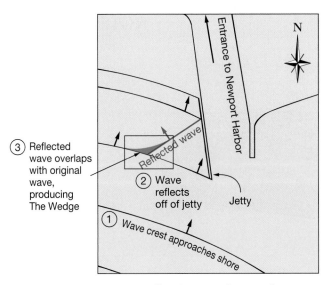

Figure 8.19   Wave reflection at The Wedge, Newport Harbor, California

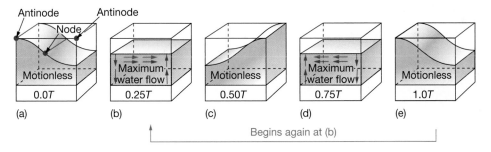

Figure 8.20   Sequence of motion in a standing wave

NOTES:

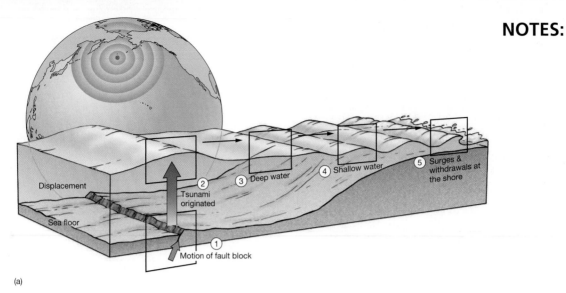

(a)

Figure 8.21a Origin of a tsunami

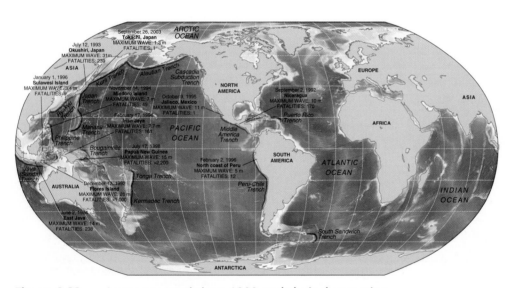

Figure 8.23 Large tsunami since 1990 and their destruction

Figure 8.25b   How a wave power plant works

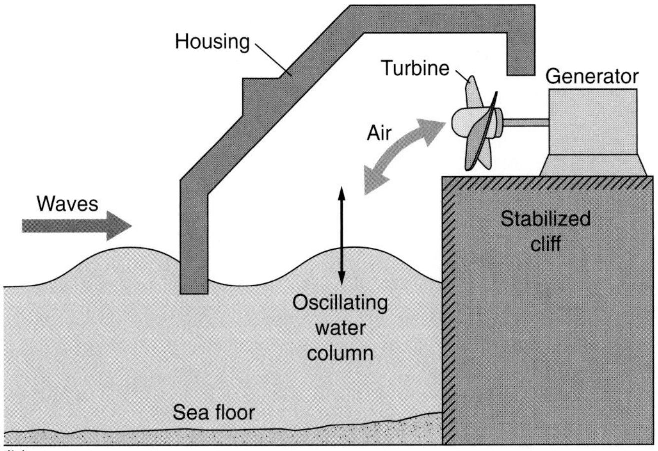

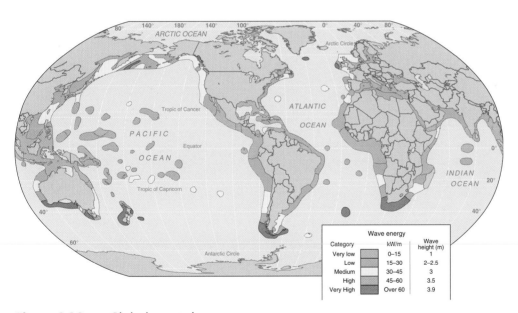

Figure 8.26   Global coastal wave energy resources

NOTES:

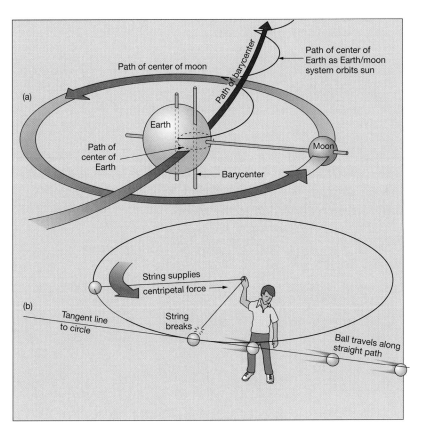

Figure 9.1   Earth-Moon system rotation

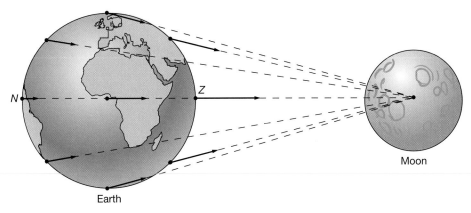

Figure 9.2   Gravitational forces on Earth due to the Moon

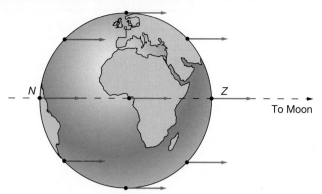

Figure 9.3   Centripetal (center-seeking) forces on Earth due to the Moon

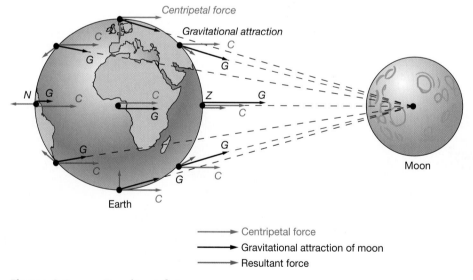

Figure 9.4   Resultant forces

NOTES:

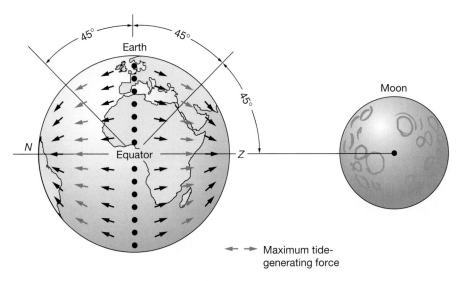

Figure 9.5   Tide-generating forces

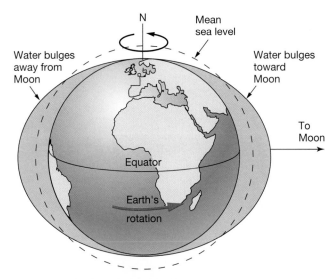

Figure 9.6   Idealized tidal bulges

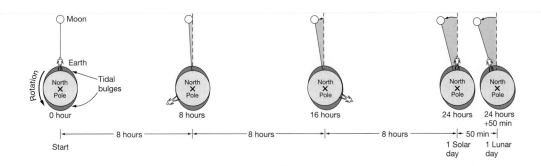

Figure 9.7   The lunar day

NOTES:

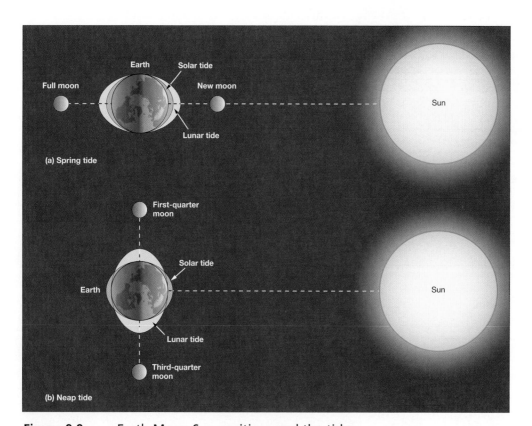

Figure 9.8   Relative sizes and distances of Earth, moon, and Sun

Figure 9.9   Earth-Moon-Sun positions and the tides

NOTES:

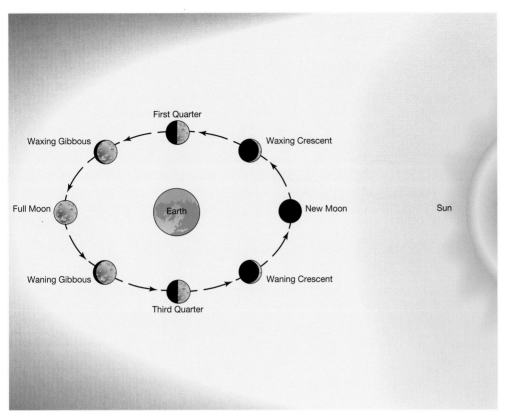

Figure 9.10   Phases of the Moon

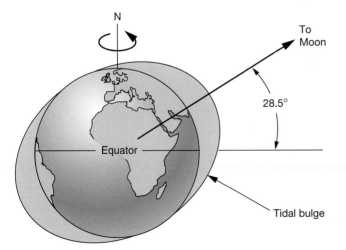

Figure 9.11   Maximum declination of tidal bulges from the equator

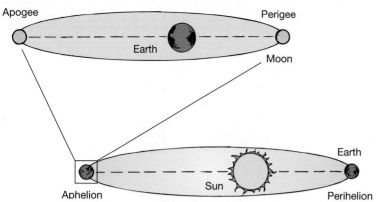

Figure 9.12   Effects of elliptical orbits

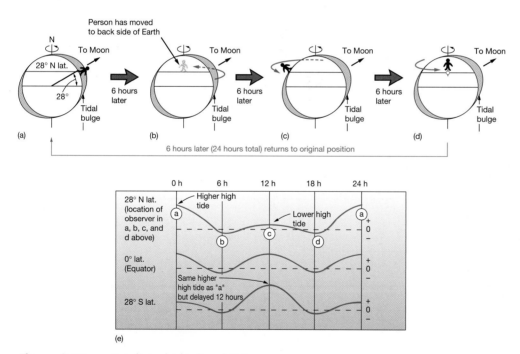

Figure 9.13   Predicted idealized tides

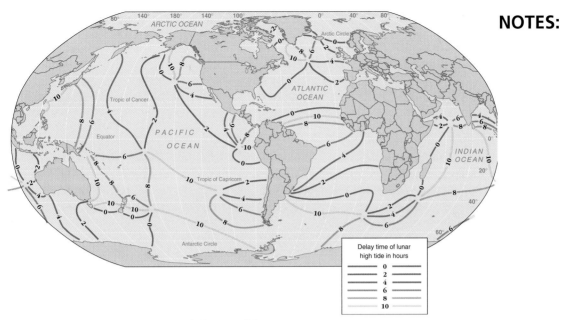

NOTES:

Figure 9.14   Cotidal map of the world

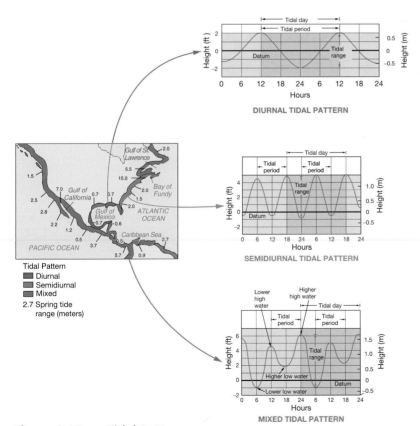

Figure 9.15   Tidal Patterns

NOTES:

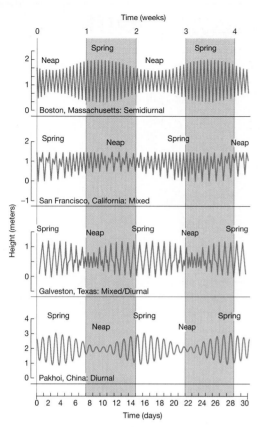

Figure 9.16   Monthly tidal curves

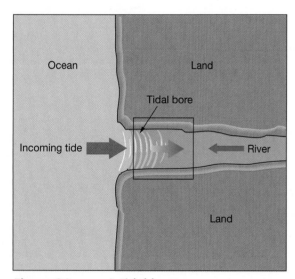

Figure 9A   A tidal bore

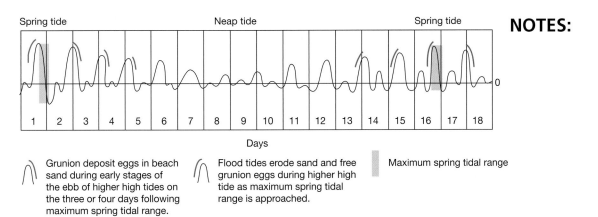

Grunion deposit eggs in beach sand during early stages of the ebb of higher high tides on the three or four days following maximum spring tidal range.

Flood tides erode sand and free grunion eggs during higher high tide as maximum spring tidal range is approached.

Maximum spring tidal range

Figure 9B   The tidal cycle

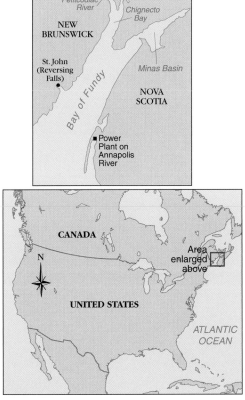

Figure 9.17   The Bay of Fundy, site of the world's largest tidal range

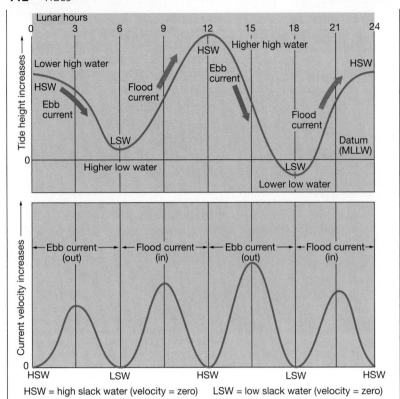

Figure 9.18   Reversing tidal currents in a bay

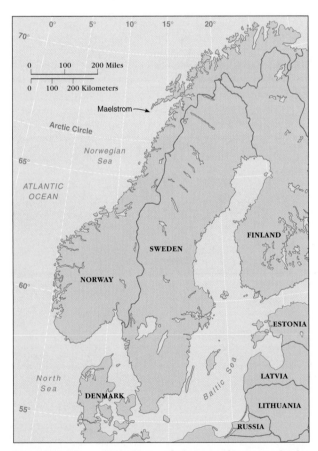

Figure 9.19   Location of the Maelstrom whirlpool

NOTES:

One tidal cycle = 12 hours 25 minutes

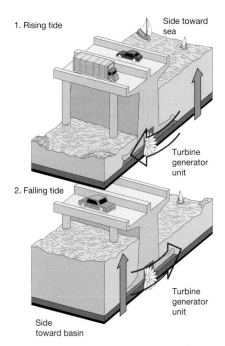

Figure 9.20   La Rance tidal power plant at St. Malo, France

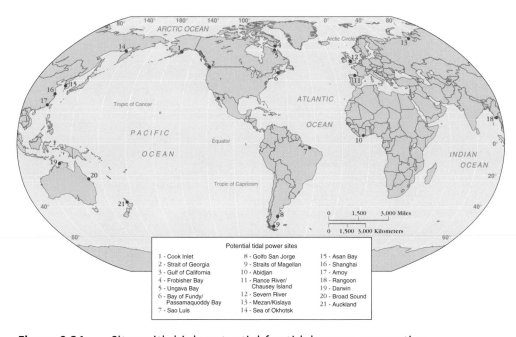

Potential tidal power sites

1 - Cook Inlet	8 - Golfo San Jorge	15 - Asan Bay
2 - Strait of Georgia	9 - Straits of Magellan	16 - Shanghai
3 - Gulf of California	10 - Abidjan	17 - Amoy
4 - Frobisher Bay	11 - Rance River/	18 - Rangoon
5 - Ungava Bay	Chausey Island	19 - Darwin
6 - Bay of Fundy/	12 - Severn River	20 - Broad Sound
Passamaquoddy Bay	13 - Mezan/Kislaya	21 - Auckland
7 - Sao Luis	14 - Sea of Okhotsk	

Figure 9.21   Sites with high potential for tidal power generation

Figure 10.1   Landforms and terminology of coastal regions

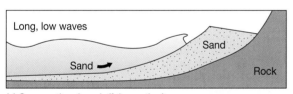

(a) Summertime beach (fair weather)

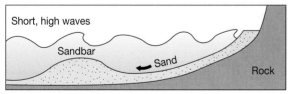

(b) Wintertime beach (storm)

Figure 10.2   Summertime and wintertime beach conditions

NOTES:

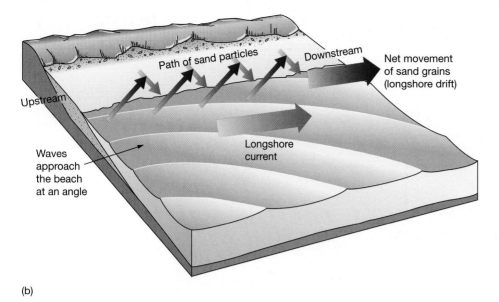

(b)

Figure 10.3b Longshore current and longshore drift

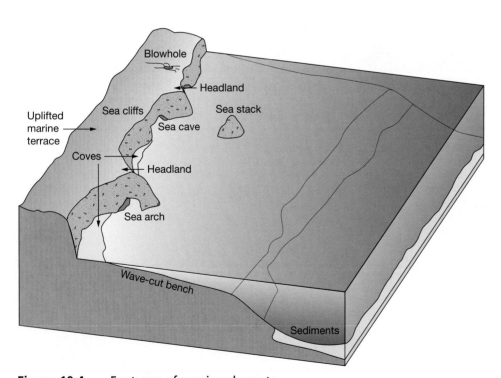

Figure 10.4 Features of erosional coasts

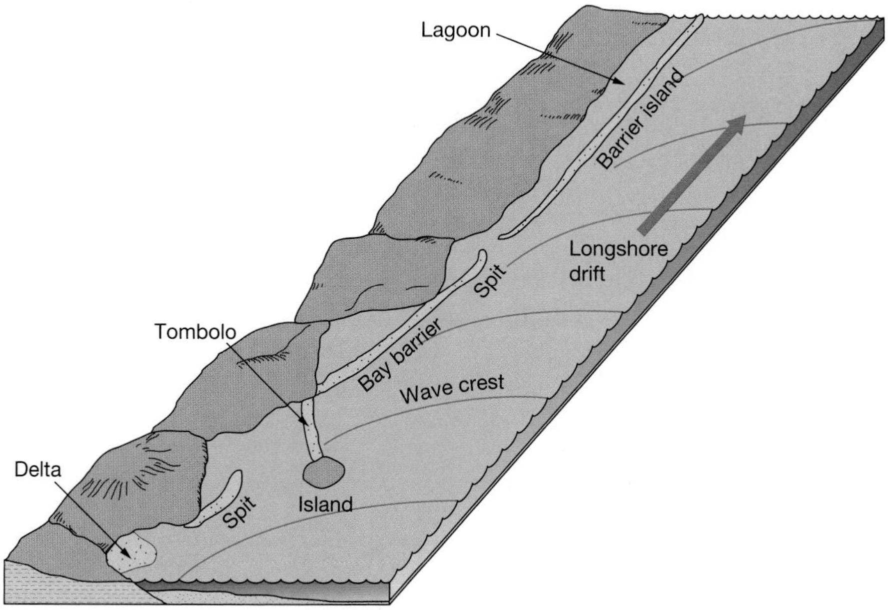

NOTES:

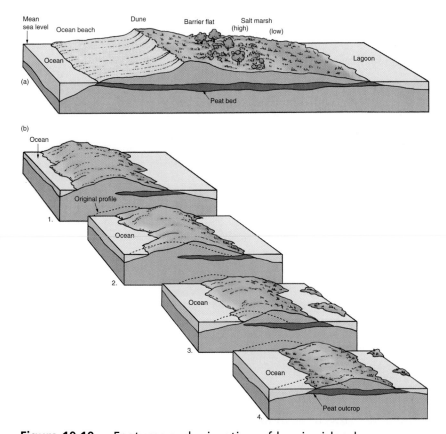

Figure 10.7   Features of depositional coasts

Figure 10.10   Features and migration of barrier islands

NOTES:

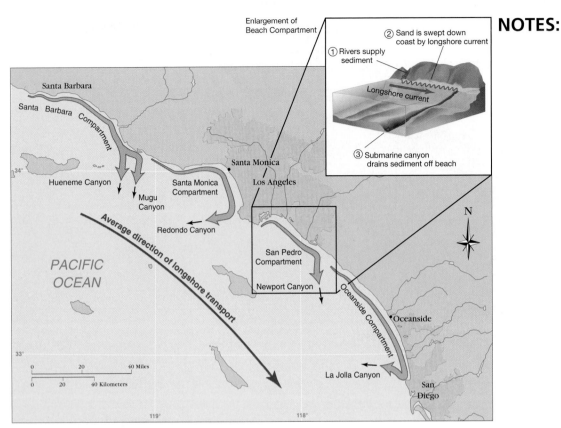

Figure 10.12   Beach compartments

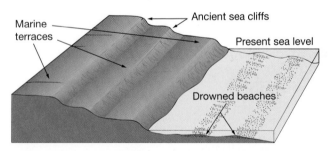

Figure 10.13   Evidence of ancient shorelines

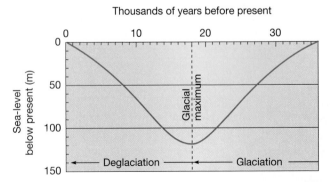

Figure 10.14   Sea level change during the most recent advance and retreat of Pleistocene glaciers

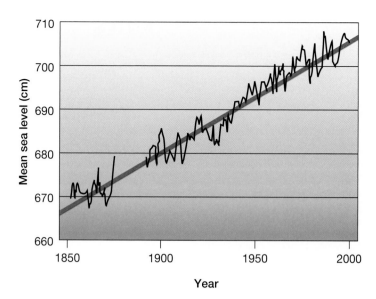

Figure 10.15   Measured relative sea level rise at New York City

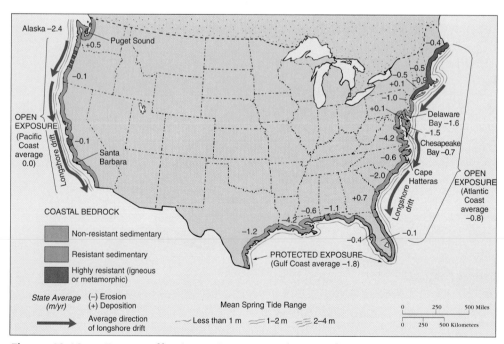

Figure 10.16   Factors affecting U.S. coasts and rates of erosion and deposition

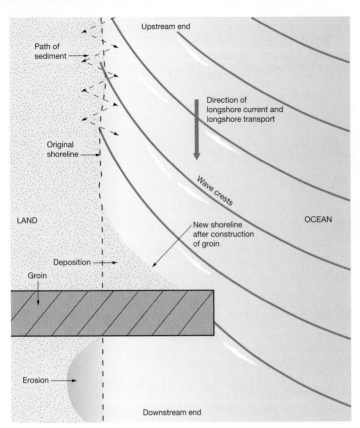

Figure 10.19 Interference of sand movement

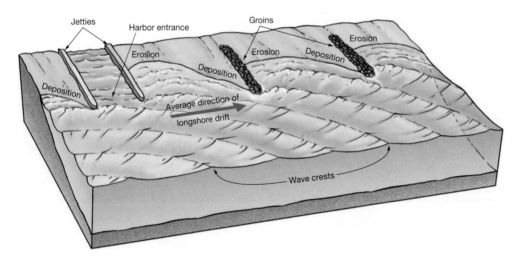

Figure 10.21 Jetties and groins

NOTES:

Old sea cliff

Santa Barbara Harbor

Breakwater

Dredge

Dredge discharge

Area threatened by erosion after harbor breakwater was built

Pier

New deposition

Wave crest

Average direction of longshore drift

Figure 10.23 Breakwater at Santa Barbara Harbor, California

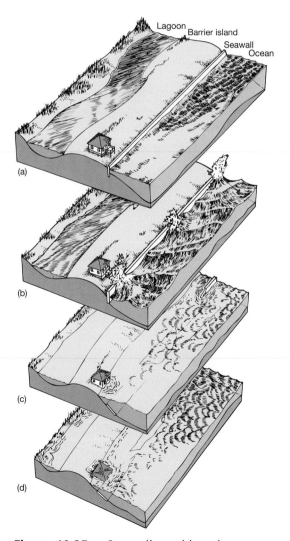

Lagoon

Barrier island

Seawall

Ocean

(a)

(b)

(c)

(d)

Figure 10.25 Seawalls and beaches

NOTES:

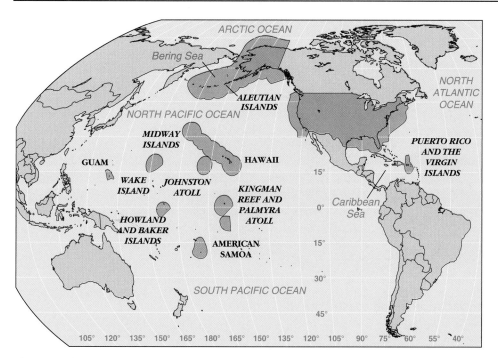

Figure 11.1   The Exclusive Economic Zone (EEZ) of the United States

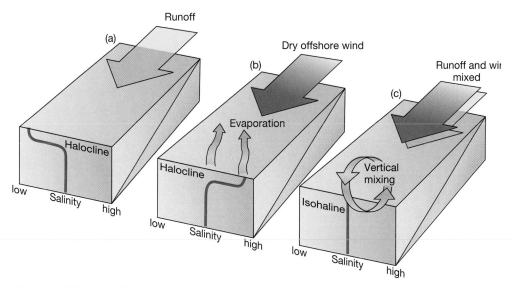

Figure 11.2   Salinity variation in the coastal ocean

NOTES:

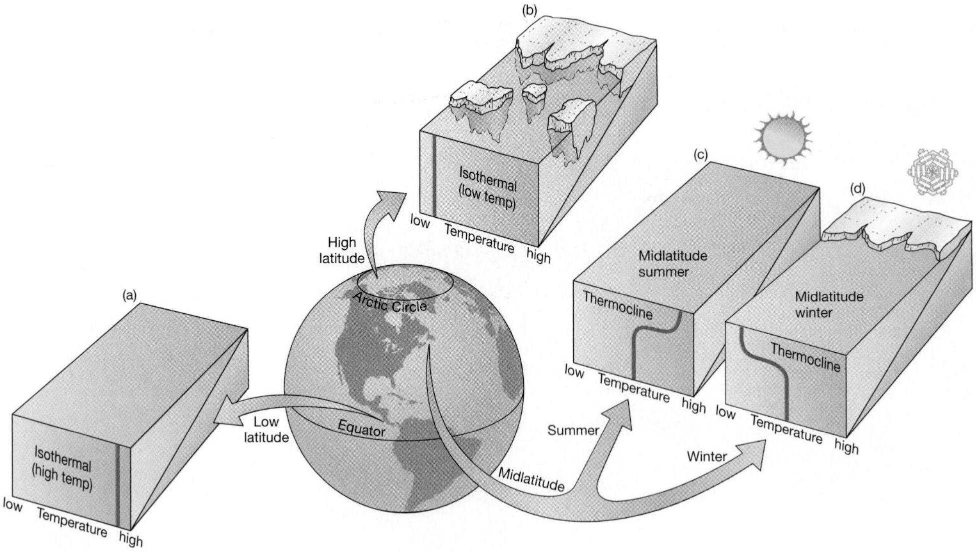

Figure 11.3   Temperature variation in the coastal ocean

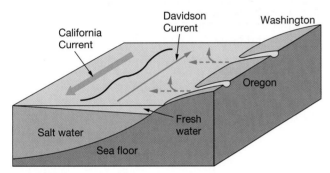

Figure 11.4   Davidson coastal geostrophic current

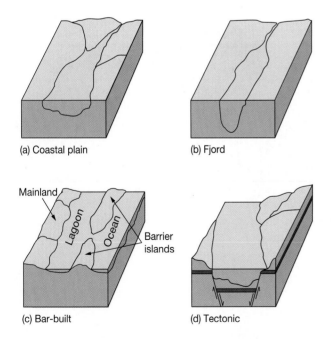

(a) Coastal plain

(b) Fjord

(c) Bar-built

(d) Tectonic

Figure 11.5   Classifying estuaries by origin

NOTES:

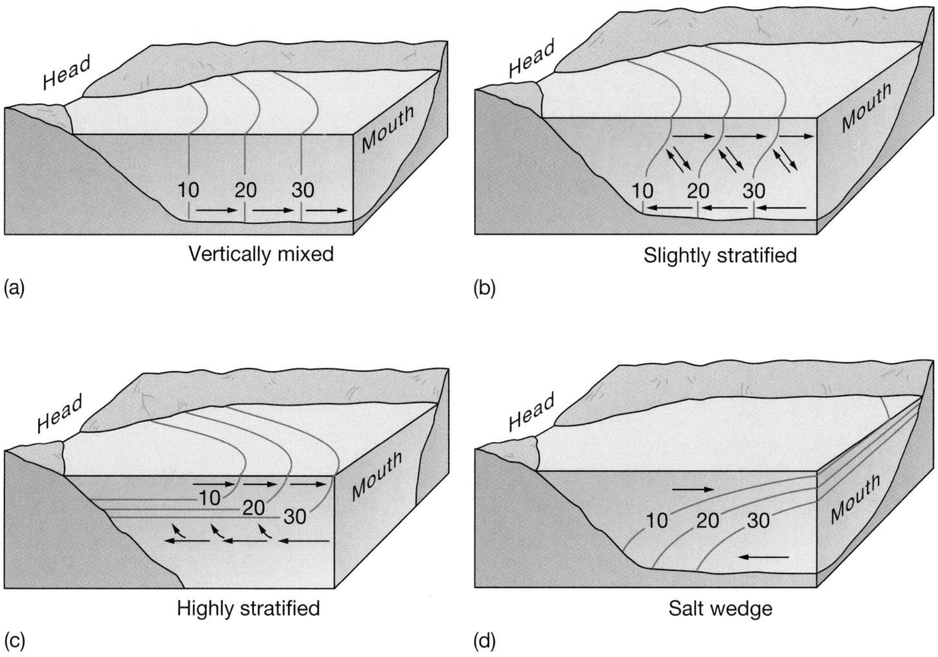

(a)
Vertically mixed

(b)
Slightly stratified

(c)
Highly stratified

(d)
Salt wedge

Figure 11.7 Classifying estuaries by mixing

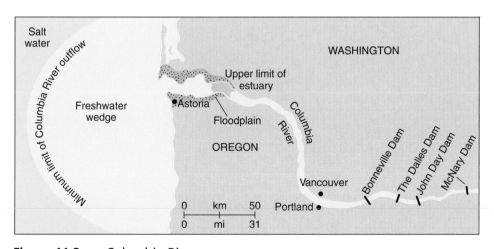

Figure 11.8 Columbia River

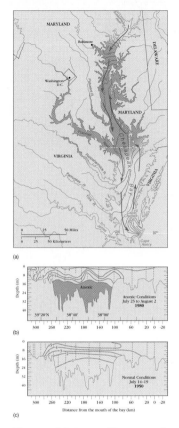

(a)

(b)

(c)

Figure 11.9 Chesapeake Bay

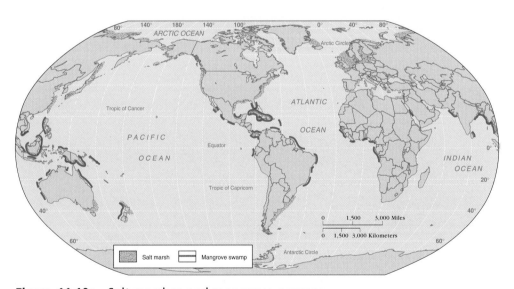

Figure 11.10a Salt marshes and mangrove swamps

NOTES:

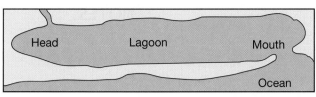

(a) Geometry

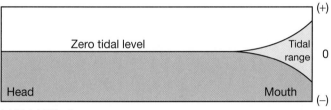

(b) Salinity

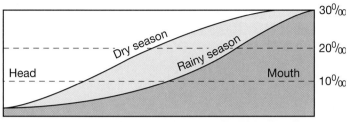

(c) Tidal Effects

Figure 11.11   Lagoons

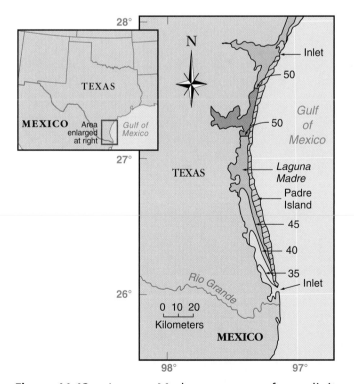

Figure 11.12   Laguna Madre summer surface salinity

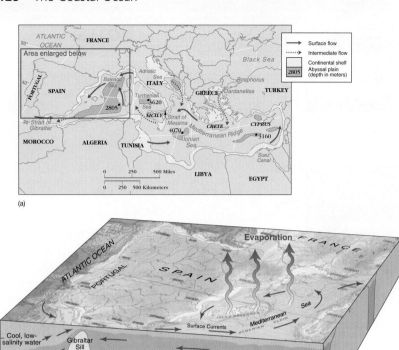

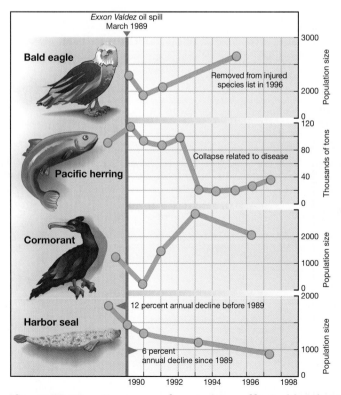

Figure 11.13 Mediterranean Sea bathymetry and circulation

Figure 11.15 Recovery of organisms affected by the *Exxon Valdez* oil spill

NOTES:

NOTES:

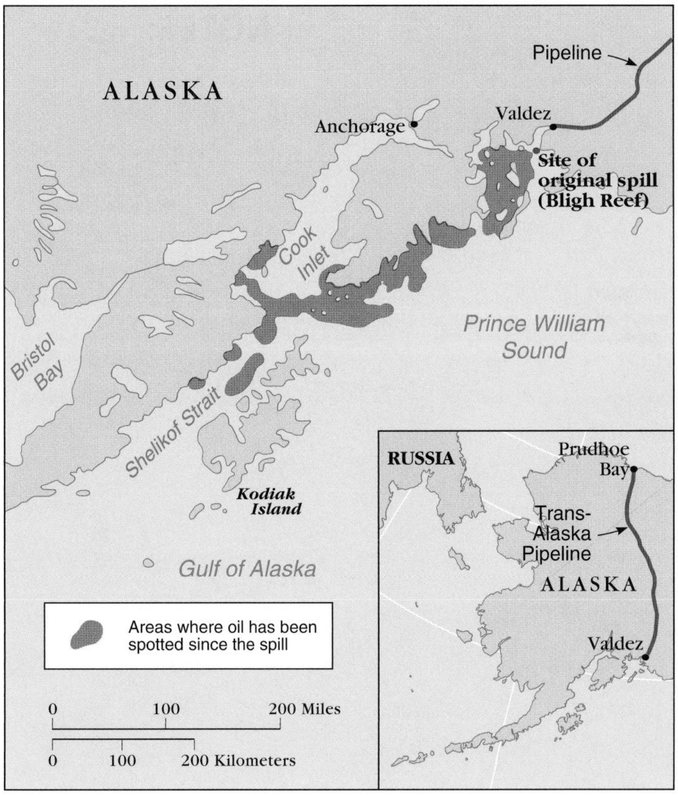

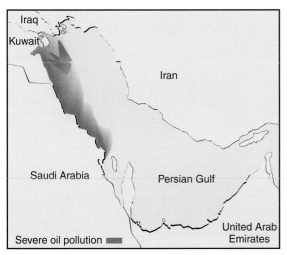

Figure 11A The 1989 Exxon Valdez oil spill, Prince William Sound, Alaska

Figure 11B Oil pollution from the 1991 Persian Gulf War

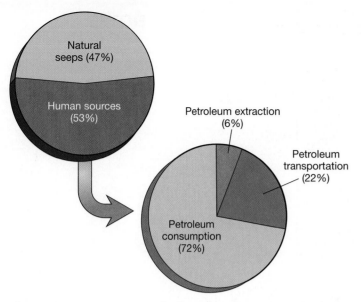

NOTES:

Figure 11.17 Sources of oil to the oceans

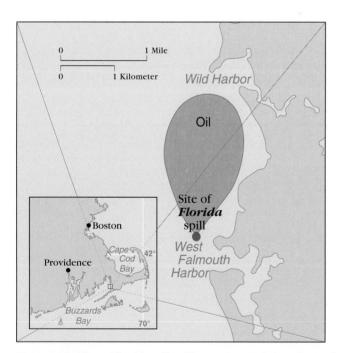

Figure 11.18 *Florida* oil spill at West Falmouth Harbor, Massachusetts

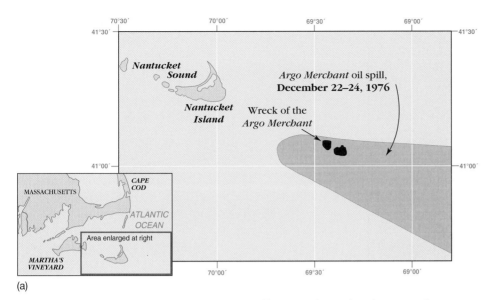

Figure 11.19a *Argo Merchant* oil spill off Nantucket Island, Massachusetts

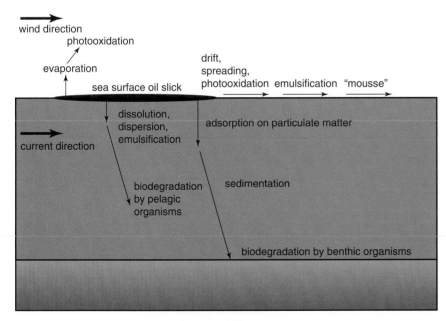

Figure 11.21   Processes acting on oil spills

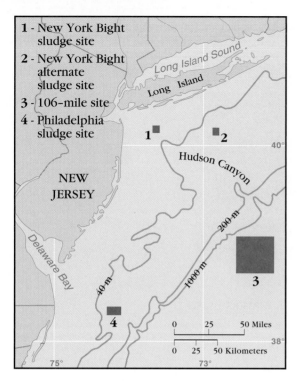

NOTES:

Figure 11.24   Atlantic sewage sludge disposal sites

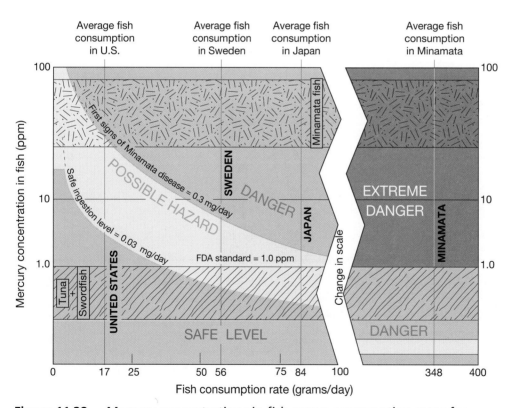

Figure 11.28   Mercury concentrations in fish versus consumption rates for various populations

NOTES:

Under the MARPOL agreement and U.S. federal law, it is illegal for any vessel to discharge plastics or garbage containing plastics into any waters. Additional restrictions on dumping non-plastic waste are outlined below. All discharge of garbage is prohibited in the Great Lakes or their connecting or tributary waters. Each knowing violation of these requirements may result in a fine of up to $500,000 and 6 years imprisonment.

Within 3 nautical miles of shore and anywhere in lakes, rivers, bays, and sounds.

ILLEGAL TO DUMP
Plastic
All other trash

3 to 12 nautical miles offshore

ILLEGAL TO DUMP
Plastic
Dunnage, lining & packing materials that float
All other trash if not ground to less than 1"

12 to 25 nautical miles offshore

ILLEGAL TO DUMP
Plastic
Dunnage, lining & packing materials that float

Outside 25 nautical miles offshore

ILLEGAL TO DUMP
Plastic

State and local laws may place further restrictions on the disposal of garbage.

WORKING TOGETHER, WE CAN ALL MAKE A DIFFERENCE!
CENTER FOR MARINE CONSERVATION 1725 DeSales Street, NW Washington, DC 20036 (202)429-5609

Figure 11.30   Current law regulating ocean dumping

NOTES:

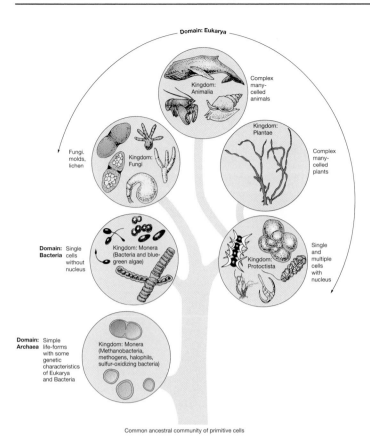

Figure 12.2   Phytoplankton and zooplankton (floaters)

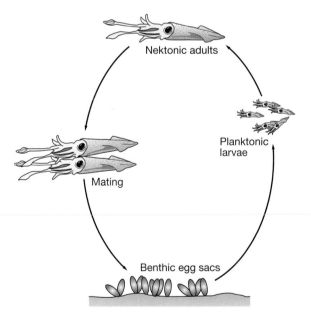

Figure 12.3   Typical life cycle of a squid

NOTES:

Figure 12.4   Nekton (swimmers)

Figure 12.5   Benthos (bottom dwellers): representative intertidal and
shallow subtidal forms

NOTES:

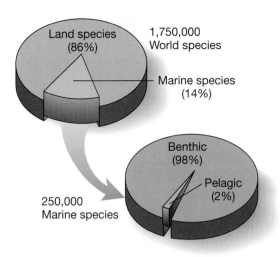

Figure 12.6   Distribution of species on Earth

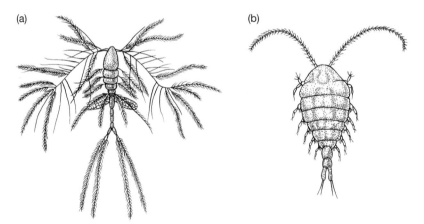

Figure 12.7   Water temperature and appendages

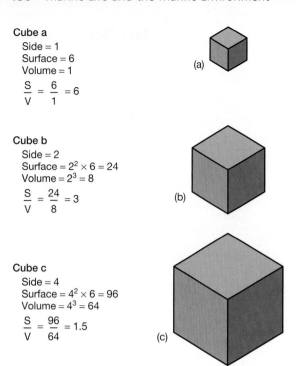

Cube a
Side = 1
Surface = 6
Volume = 1
$$\frac{S}{V} = \frac{6}{1} = 6$$

Cube b
Side = 2
Surface = $2^2 \times 6 = 24$
Volume = $2^3 = 8$
$$\frac{S}{V} = \frac{24}{8} = 3$$

Cube c
Side = 4
Surface = $4^2 \times 6 = 96$
Volume = $4^3 = 64$
$$\frac{S}{V} = \frac{96}{64} = 1.5$$

Figure 12.8 Surface area to volume ratio of cubes of different sizes

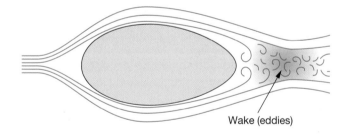

Wake (eddies)

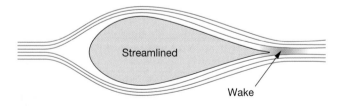

Streamlined

Wake

Figure 12.10 Streamlining

NOTES:

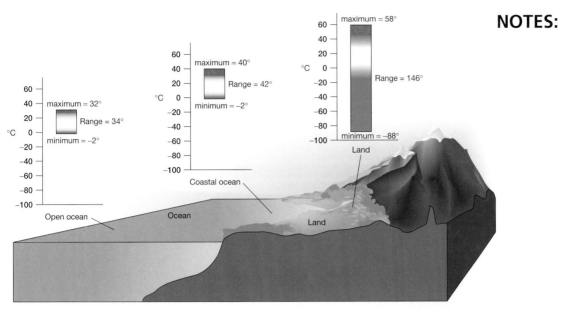

Figure 12.11   A comparison of extremes in ocean and land surface temperatures

DIFFUSION

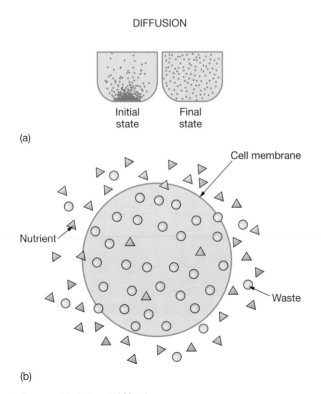

Figure 12.12   Diffusion

OSMOSIS

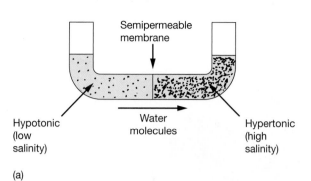

Semipermeable membrane

Hypotonic (low salinity)

Water molecules

Hypertonic (high salinity)

(a)

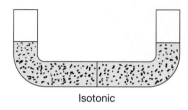

Isotonic

(b)

Figure 12.13 Osmosis

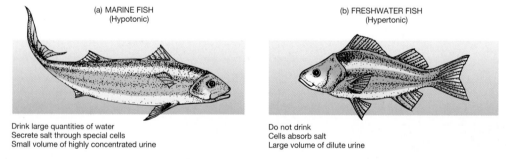

(a) MARINE FISH (Hypotonic)

(b) FRESHWATER FISH (Hypertonic)

Drink large quantities of water
Secrete salt through special cells
Small volume of highly concentrated urine

Do not drink
Cells absorb salt
Large volume of dilute urine

Figure 12.14 Salinity adaptations of marine and freshwater fish

NOTES:

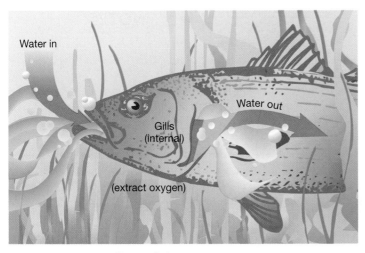

Figure 12.15   Gills on fish

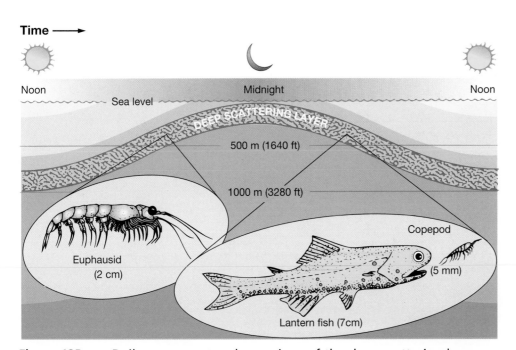

Figure 12B   Daily movement and organisms of the deep scattering layer

NOTES:

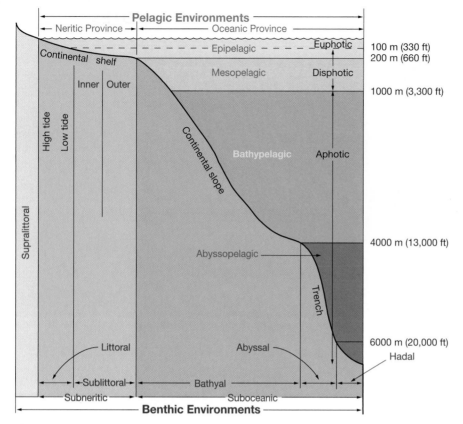

Figure 12.19   Oceanic biozones of the pelagic and benthic environments

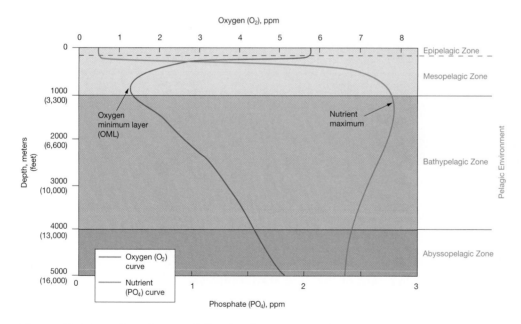

Figure 12.20   Abundance of dissolved oxygen and nutrients with depth

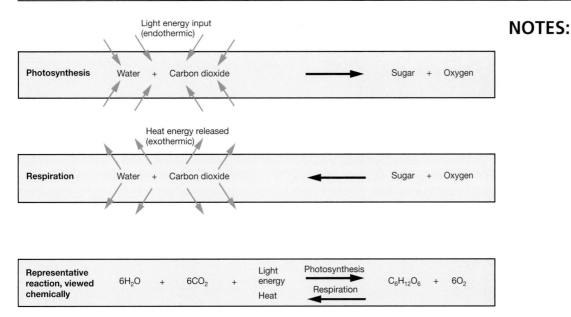

NOTES:

Figure 13.1   Primary productivity in photosynthesis, respiration and representative reactions viewed chemically.

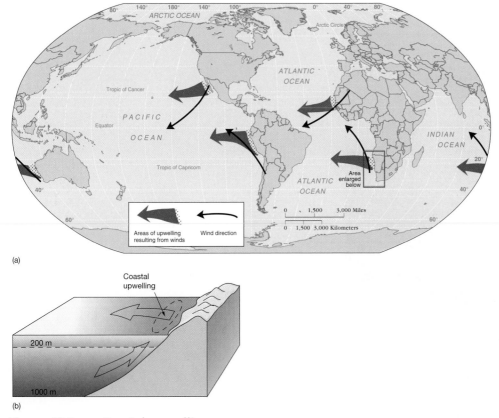

Figure 13.3   Coastal upwelling

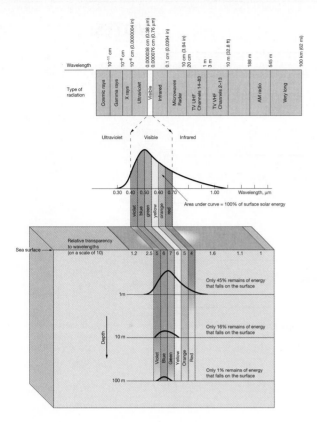

Figure 13.4   The electromagnetic spectrum and transmission of visible light in seawater

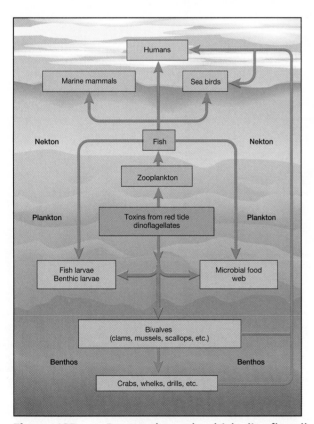

Figure 13B   Routes through which dinoflagellate toxins spread to marine organisms and humans

NOTES:

NOTES:

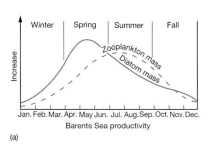

(a)

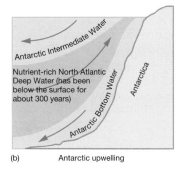

(b)   Antarctic upwelling

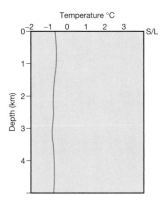

(c)

Figure 13.11   Productivity in polar oceans

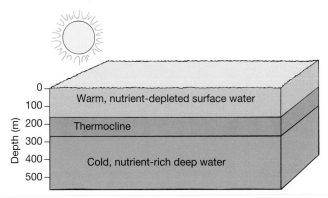

Figure 13.12   Productivity in tropical oceans

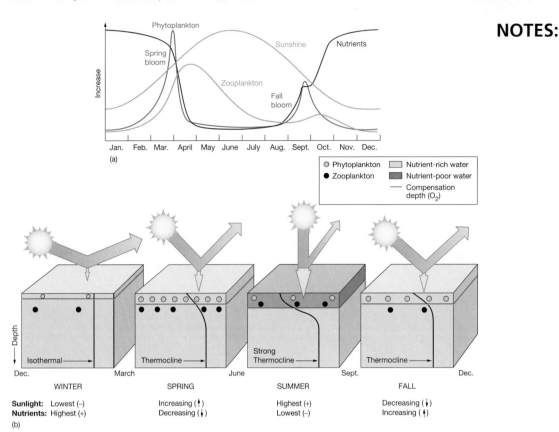

Figure 13.13   Productivity in temperature oceans (Northern Hemisphere)

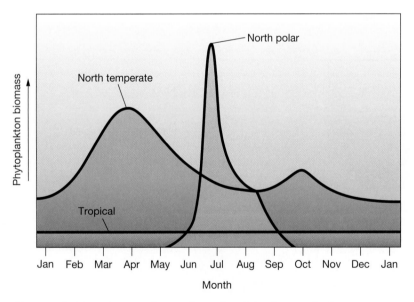

Figure 13.14   Comparison of productivity in tropical, temperature, and polar oceans (Northern Hemisphere)

NOTES:

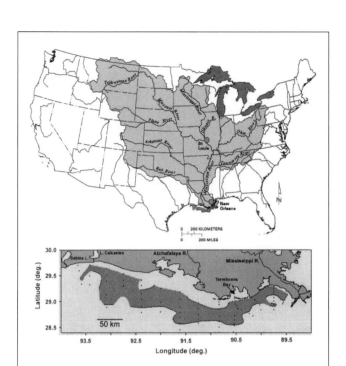

Figure 13F   The Gulf of Mexico "dead zone"

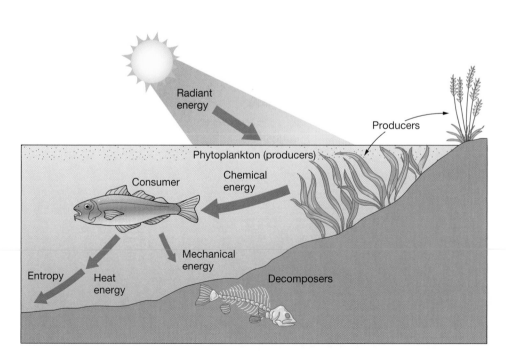

Figure 13.15   Energy flow through a photosynthetic marine ecosystem

NOTES:

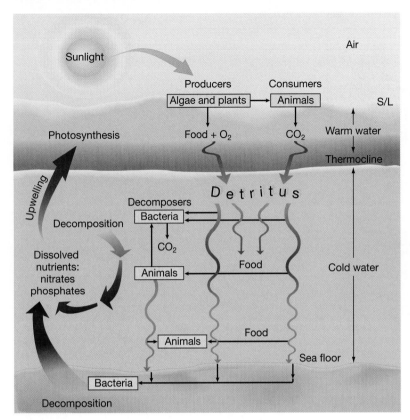

Figure 13.16 Biogeochemical cycling of matter

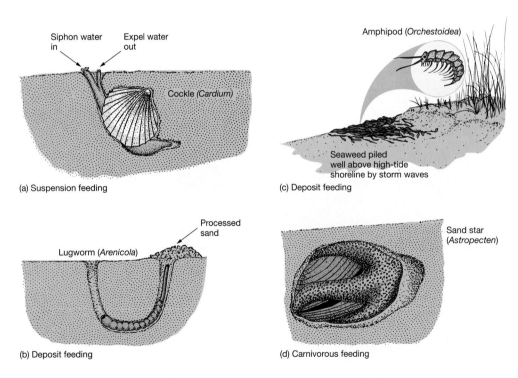

Figure 13.17 Modes of feeding along sediment-covered shores

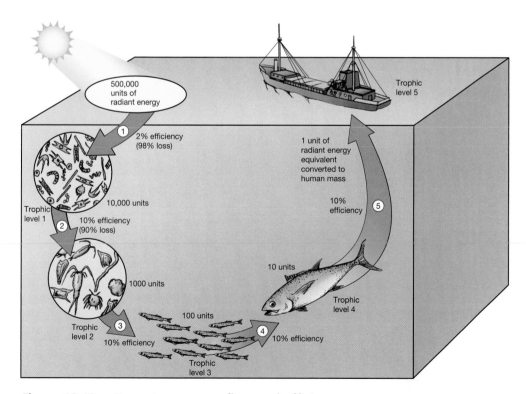

NOTES:

Producers ⟵ Herbivores ⟶ Carnivores

Phytoplankton mass

Mass eaten by herbivores

Assimilated by herbivores

Increased mass through growth and reproduction

Eaten by carnivores

Dies Uneaten

Respiration

Feces

Figure 13.18   Passage of energy through a trophic level

500,000 units of radiant energy

1 2% efficiency (98% loss)

1 unit of radiant energy equivalent converted to human mass

Trophic level 5

Trophic level 1

10,000 units

2 10% efficiency (90% loss)

10% efficiency

5

1000 units

Trophic level 2

3 10% efficiency

100 units

10 units

Trophic level 4

4 10% efficiency

Trophic level 3

Figure 13.19   Ecosystem energy flow and efficiency

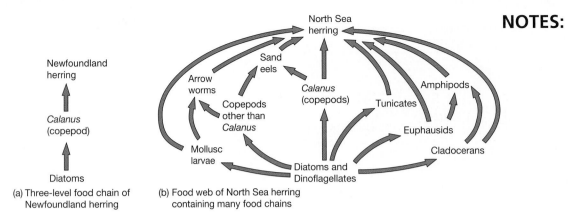

(a) Three-level food chain of
   Newfoundland herring

(b) Food web of North Sea herring
   containing many food chains

Figure 13.20   Comparison between a food chain and a food web

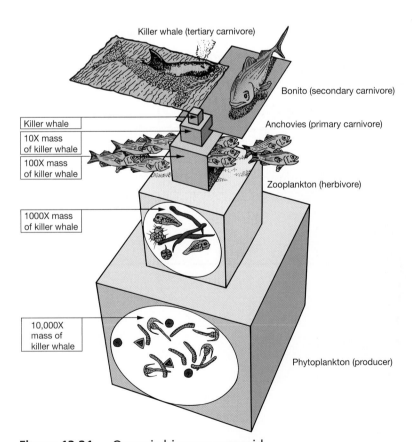

Figure 13.21   Oceanic biomass pyramid

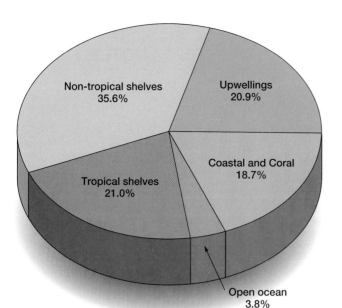

Figure 13.23   Marine fishery ecosystems

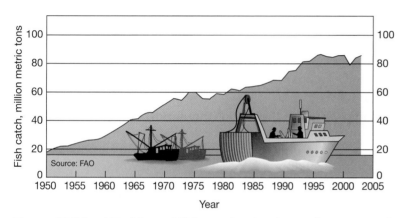

Figure 13.24   World total fish production in marine waters since 1950

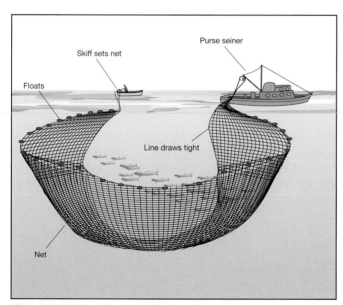

Figure 13.26   Purse seiner

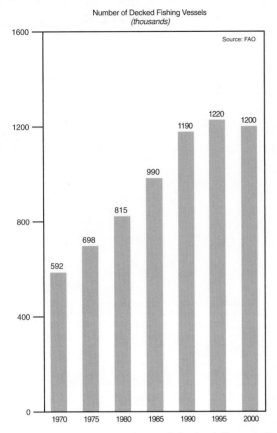

Figure 13.27 Number of decked (large) fishing vessels in the world (thousands)

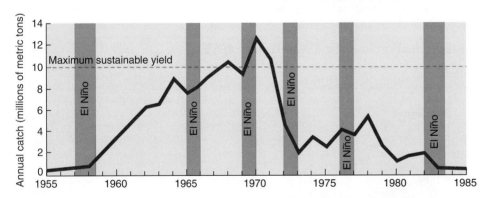

Figure 13G Peruvian anchovies and annual catch, 1955–1985

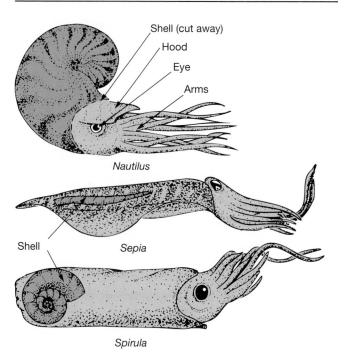

Shell (cut away)
Hood
Eye
Arms

Nautilus

Sepia

Shell

Spirula

Figure 14.1   Gas containers in cephalopods

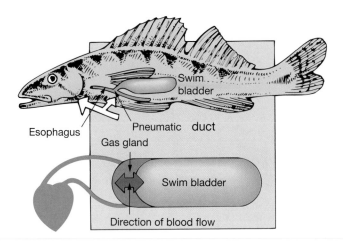

Swim bladder

Esophagus

Pneumatic duct

Gas gland

Swim bladder

Direction of blood flow

Figure 14.2   Swim bladder

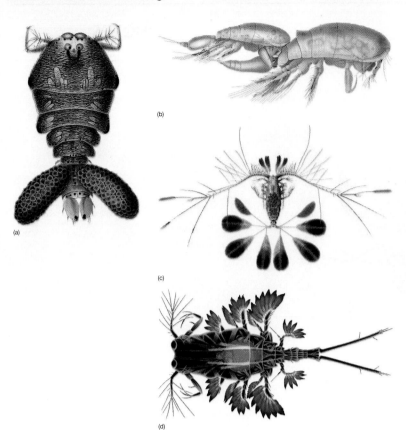

(a)

(b)

(c)

(d)

Figure 14.5   Copepods

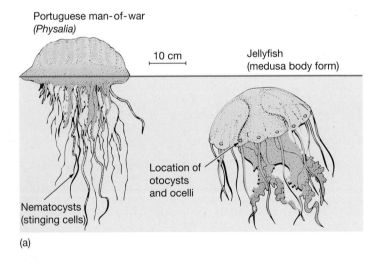

Portuguese man-of-war
(Physalia)

10 cm

Jellyfish
(medusa body form)

Location of
otocysts
and ocelli

Nematocysts
(stinging cells)

(a)

Figure 14.7a   Planktonic cnidarins

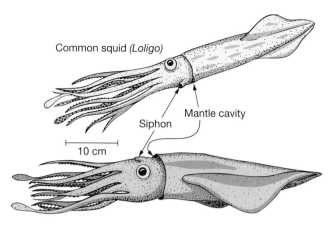

Common squid *(Loligo)*

Mantle cavity

Siphon

10 cm

Flying squid *(Ommastrephes)*

Figure 14.8   Squid

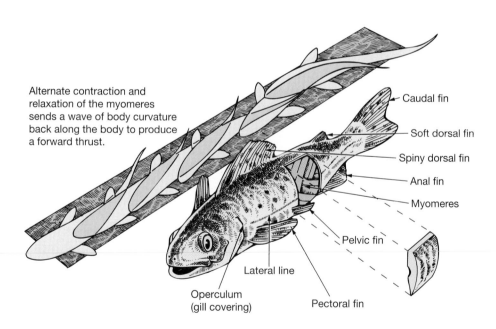

Alternate contraction and relaxation of the myomeres sends a wave of body curvature back along the body to produce a forward thrust.

Caudal fin

Soft dorsal fin

Spiny dorsal fin

Anal fin

Myomeres

Pelvic fin

Lateral line

Operculum (gill covering)

Pectoral fin

Figure 14.9   Swimming motions and general features of fish

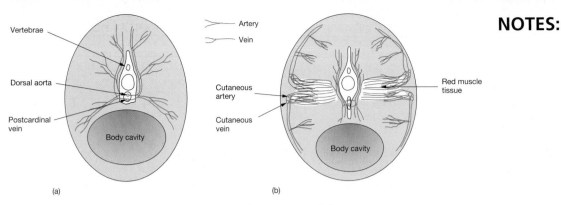

Figure 14.12 Circulatory system modifications in fish

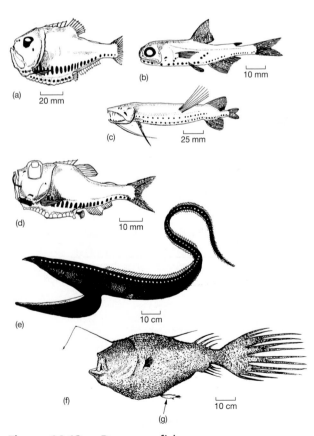

Figure 14.13 Deep-sea fish

NOTES:

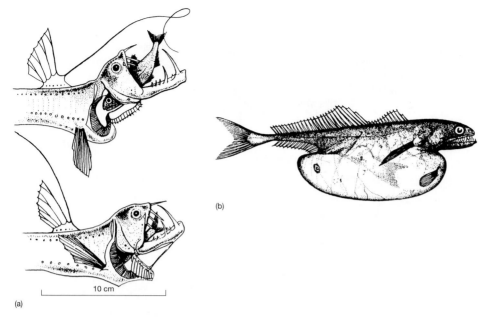

(b)

(a)

Figure 14.14 Adaptations of deep-sea fish

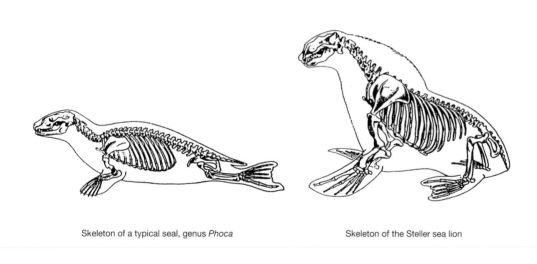

Skeleton of a typical seal, genus *Phoca*

Skeleton of the Steller sea lion

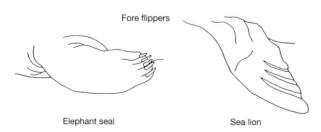

Fore flippers

Elephant seal

Sea lion

Figure 14.17 Skeletal and morphological differences between seals and sea lions

Figure 14.19 Marine mammals of order Cetacea

NOTES:

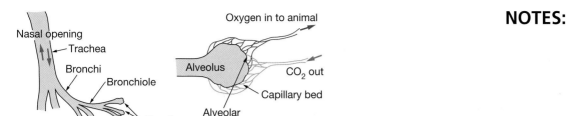

NOTES:

Figure 14.20 (right)   Cetacean modifications to allow prolonged submergence

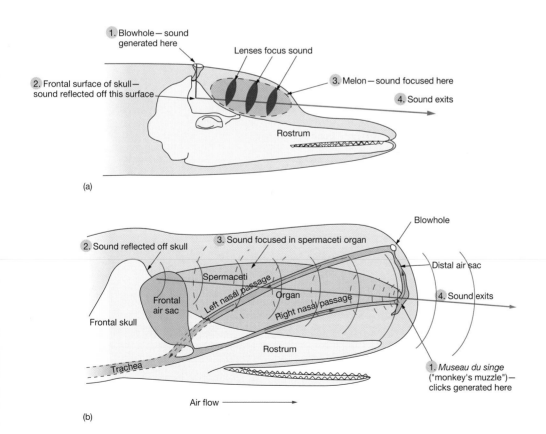

Figure 14.22   Generation of echolocation clicks in small toothed and sperm whales

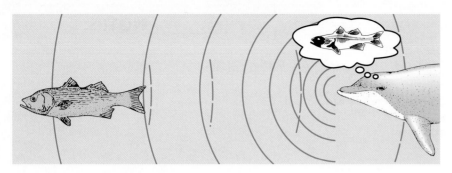

NOTES:

Figure 14.23   Echolocation

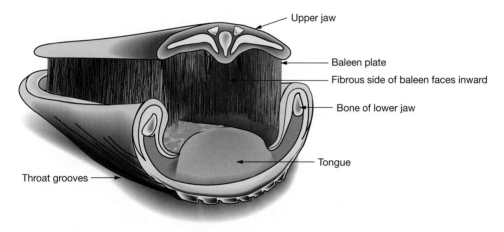

Upper jaw

Baleen plate

Fibrous side of baleen faces inward

Bone of lower jaw

Tongue

Throat grooves

Figure 14.24a   Baleen

NOTES:

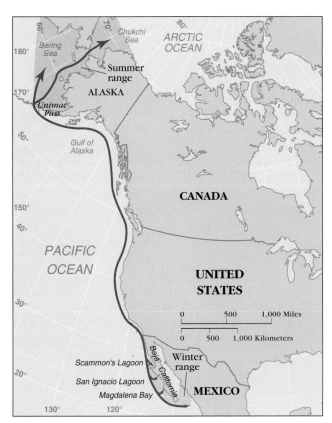

Figure 14.26   Gray whale migration route

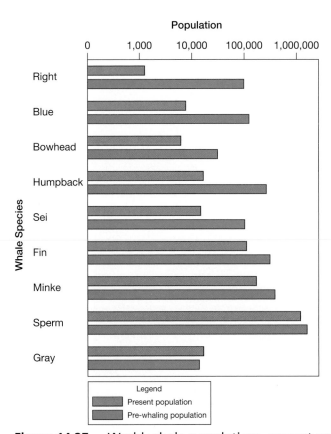

Figure 14.27   World whale population: present and pre-whaling

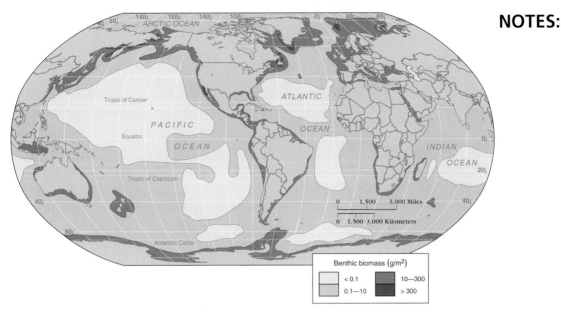

NOTES:

Figure 15.1   Oceanic benthic biomass

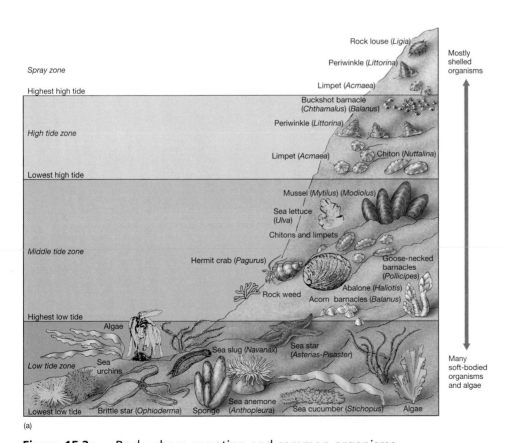

(a)

Figure 15.2a   Rocky shore zonation and common organisms

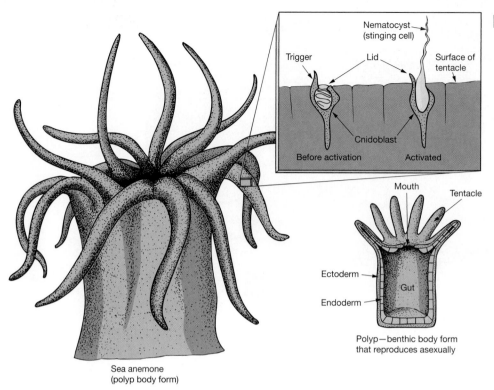

Figure 15.4   Sea anemone structure and operation of its stinging cells

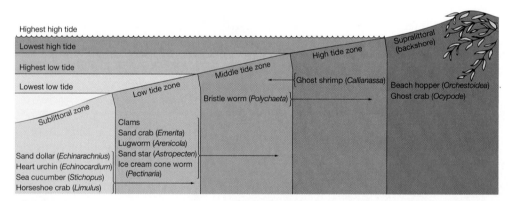

Figure 15.8   Interidal zonation and typical organisms on a sediment-covered shore

NOTES:

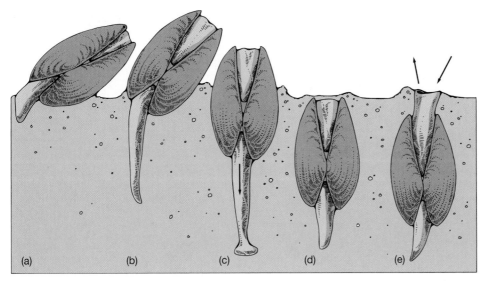

Figure 15.9   How a clam burrows

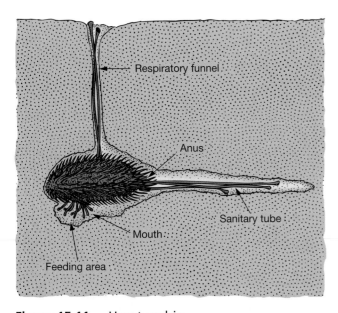

Respiratory funnel

Anus

Sanitary tube

Mouth

Feeding area

Figure 15.11   Heart urchin

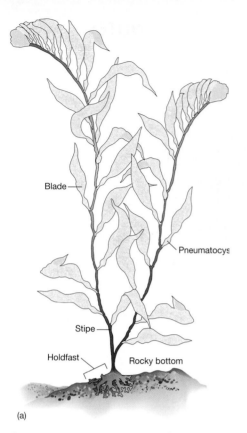

(a)

Figure 15.14a   Structure of the giant brown bladder kelp

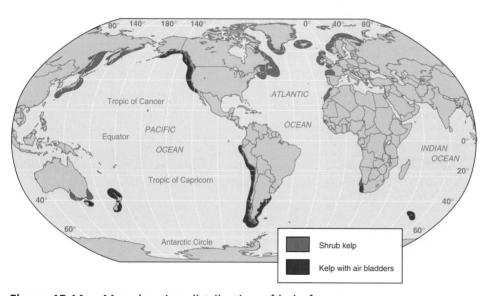

Figure 15.14c   Map showing distribution of kelp forests

NOTES:

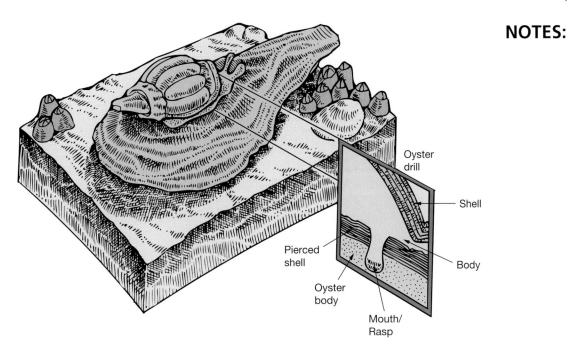

Figure 15.16   An oyster drill snail feeding on an oyster

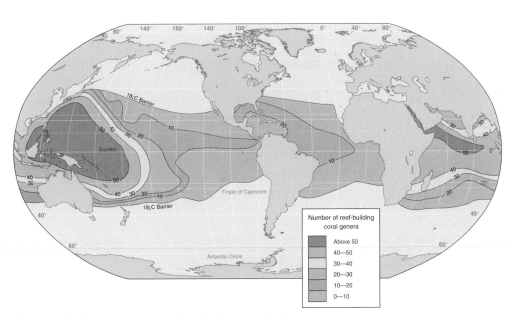

Figure 15.17   Coral reef distribution and diversity

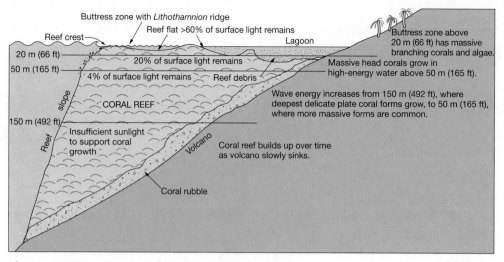

Figure 15.19   Coral reef zonation

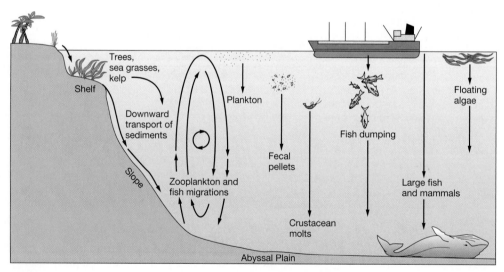

Figure 15.22   Food sources for deep-sea organisms

NOTES:

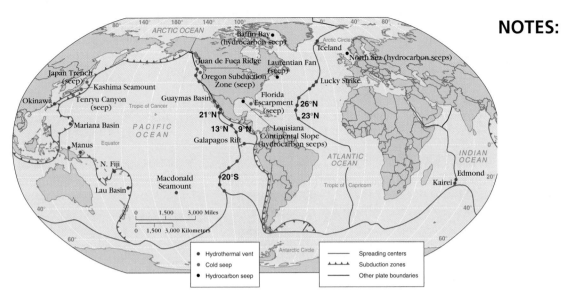

Figure 15.24   Vents and seeps known to support deep-sea biocommunities

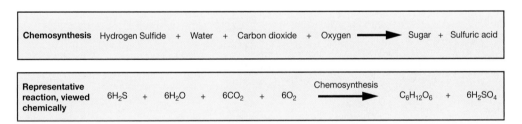

Figure 15.25   Chemosynthesis (top) and representative reaction viewed chemically (bottom)

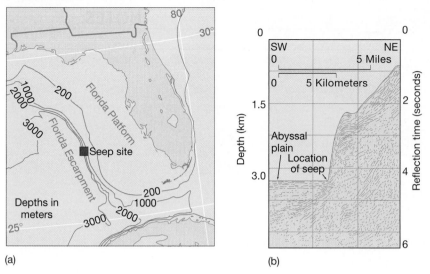

NOTES:

Figure 15.28a,b Hypersaline seep biocommunity at the base of the Florida Escarpment

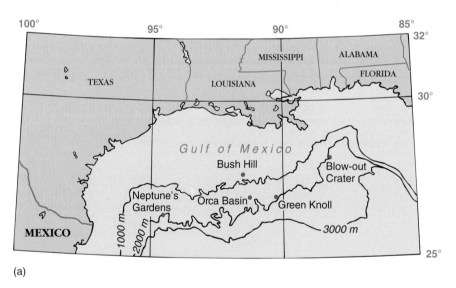

Figure 15.29a Hydrocarbon seeps on the continental slope in the Gulf of Mexico

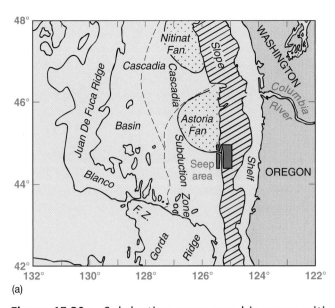

Figure 15.30a   Subduction zone seep biocommunities

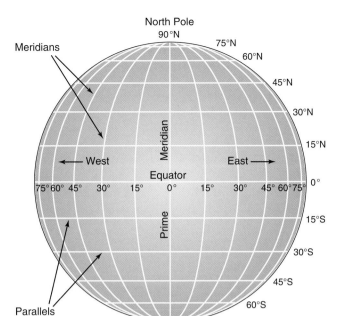

Figure A3.1   Earth's grid system

NOTES:

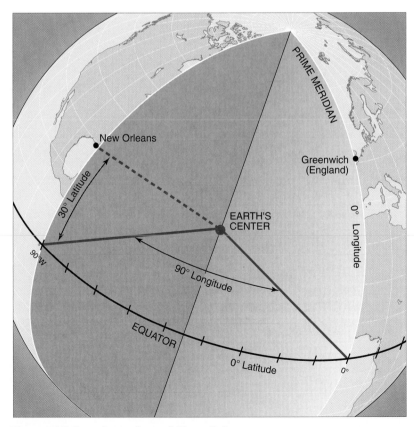

Figure A3.2   Location of New Orleans

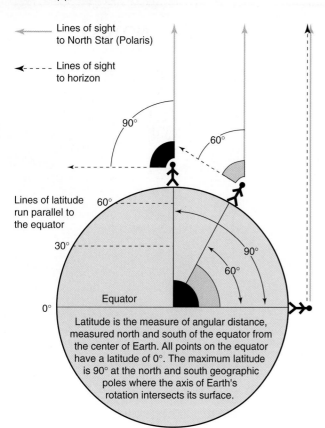

Figure A3.3   Determining latitude based on the North Star (Polaris)

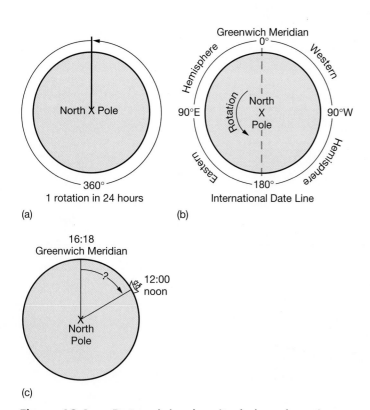

Figure A3.4   Determining longitude based on time

Periodic Table of the Elements

Light Metals																		

Legend:
- Atomic number
- Symbol of element
- Atomic weight
- Name of element
- Inert Gas
- Gas
- Liquid
- Electron (contains one negative charge)
- Number of protons (total positive charge)

Nonmetals

Transitional Elements

Heavy Metals

IA	IIA												IIIA	IVA	VA	VIA	VIIA	VIIIA
1 H 1.0080 Hydrogen																		2 He 4.003 Helium
3 Li 6.939 Lithium	4 Be 9.012 Beryllium												5 B 10.81 Boron	6 C 12.011 Carbon	7 N 14.007 Nitrogen	8 O 15.994 Oxygen	9 F 18.998 Fluorine	10 Ne 20.1863 Neon
11 Na 22.990 Sodium	12 Mg 24.31 Magnesium	IIIB	IVB	VB	VIB	VIIB		VIIIB		IB	IIB		13 Al 26.98 Aluminum	14 Si 28.09 Silicon	15 P 30.974 Phosphorus	16 S 32.064 Sulphur	17 Cl 35.453 Chlorine	18 Ar 39.948 Argon
19 K 39.102 Potassium	20 Ca 40.08 Calcium	21 Sc 44.96 Scandium	22 Ti 47.90 Titanium	23 V 50.94 Vanadium	24 Cr 52.00 Chromium	25 Mn 54.94 Manganese	26 Fe 55.85 Iron	27 Co 58.93 Cobalt	28 Ni 58.71 Nickel	29 Cu 63.54 Copper	30 Zn 65.37 Zinc		31 Ga 69.72 Gallium	32 Ge 72.59 Germanium	33 As 74.92 Arsenic	34 Se 78.96 Selenium	35 Br 79.909 Bromine	36 Kr 83.80 Krypton
37 Rb 85.47 Rubidium	38 Sr 87.62 Strontium	39 Y 88.91 Yttrium	40 Zr 91.22 Zirconium	41 Nb 92.91 Niobium	42 Mo 95.94 Molybdenum	43 Tc (99) Technetium	44 Ru 101.1 Ruthenium	45 Rh 102.90 Rhodium	46 Pd 106.4 Palladium	47 Ag 107.870 Silver	48 Cd 112.40 Cadmium		49 In 114.82 Indium	50 Sn 118.69 Tin	51 Sb 121.75 Antimony	52 Te 127.60 Tellurium	53 I 126.90 Iodine	54 Xe 131.30 Xenon
55 Cs 132.91 Cesium	56 Ba 137.34 Barium	57 TO 71	72 Hf 178.49 Hafnium	73 Ta 180.95 Tantalum	74 W 183.85 Tungsten	75 Re 186.2 Rhenium	76 Os 190.2 Osmium	77 Ir 192.2 Iridium	78 Pt 195.09 Platinum	79 Au 197.0 Gold	80 Hg 200.59 Mercury		81 Tl 204.37 Thallium	82 Pb 207.19 Lead	83 Bi 208.98 Bismuth	84 Po (210) Polonium	85 At (210) Astatine	86 Ra (222) Radon
87 Fr (223) Francium	88 Ra 226.05 Radium	89 TO 103																

	57 LA 138.91 Lanthanum	58 Ce 140.12 Cerium	59 Pr 140.91 Praseodymium	60 Nd 144.24 Neodymium	61 Pm (147) Promethium	62 Sm 150.35 Samarium	63 Eu 157.25 Europium	64 Gd 158.92 Gadolinium	65 Tb 158.92 Terbium	66 Dy 162.50 Dysprosium	67 Ho 164.93 Holmium	68 Er 167.26 Erbium	69 Tm 168.93 Thullium	70 Yb 173.04 Ytterbium	71 Lu 174.97 Lutetium
Lanthanide series																
Actinide series	89 Ac (227) Actinium	90 Th 232.04 Thorium	91 Pa (231) Protactinium	92 U 238.03 Uranium	93 Np (237) Neptunium	94 Pu (242) Plutonium	95 Am (243) Americium	96 Cm (247) Curium	97 Bk (249) Berkelium	98 Cf (251) Californium	99 Es (254) Einsteinium	100 Fm (253) Fermium	101 Md (256) Mendelevium	102 No (256) Nobelium	103 Lw (257) Lawrencium

Figure A4.1   The periodic table of the elements

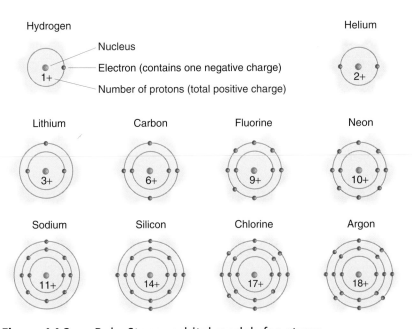

Figure A4.2   Bohr-Stoner orbital models for atoms

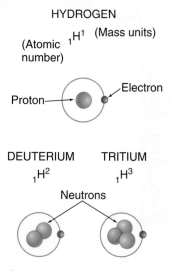

HYDROGEN

(Atomic $_1H^1$ (Mass units)
number)

Proton —— Electron

DEUTERIUM   TRITIUM
$_1H^2$ $_1H^3$

Neutrons

Figure A4.3   Hydrogen isotopes

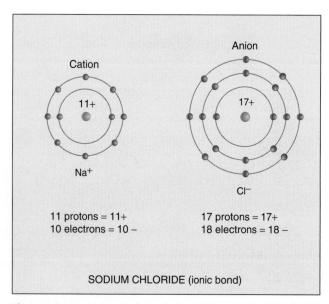

Cation

Anion

11+

17+

Na$^+$

Cl$^-$

11 protons = 11+   17 protons = 17+
10 electrons = 10 –   18 electrons = 18 –

SODIUM CHLORIDE (ionic bond)

Figure A4.4   Ionic bonds in sodium chloride (table salt)

NOTES:

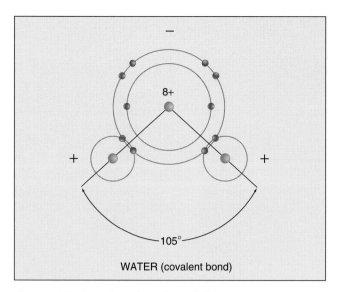

Figure A4.5   Covalent bonds in water